B

Only one passion was allowed to intrude on the ordered life of Josephine Barnes, M.A.—and that was her work. How ironic, in that case, that it should be while immersed in her latest archaeological project in Gloucestershire, that she should find not only the dig— but also her emotions—disrupted by the devastating Alex Grant!

BITTER SPRING

BY

ROWAN KIRBY

MILLS & BOON LIMITED
15–16 BROOK'S MEWS
LONDON W1A 1DR

First published 1984
Australian copyright 1984
Philippine copyright 1984
This edition 1984

© Rowan Kirby 1984

ISBN 0 263 74720 4

Set in Monophoto Plantin 10 on 10½ pt.
01–0884 – 58013

Made and printed in Great Britain by
Richard Clay (The Chaucer Press) Ltd,
Bungay, Suffolk

For
Fay, Oliver and Daniel

CHAPTER ONE

FROM the steps of her caravan, Josie was monarch of all she surveyed. This morning it was all hers: the endless green folds of Gloucestershire, punctuated by hedges and stone walls; the village not far away with its church spire and smoking cottage chimneys. And there at her feet, her own domain: the small patch of England which currently filled up her life.

She supposed it didn't look very exciting, unless you knew what it was. Glancing at it as you shot past on the main road, you might have dismissed it as any old field with a few caravans parked on one corner. True, if you had bothered to look closely you might have wondered why the soil had apparently been dug up into curious lines and patterns, or why labelled posts had been stuck into it here and there. And if you had then taken the trouble to stop and investigate properly, you'd have seen the notice at the field gate which explained everything.

Summerford Archaeological Project, it said boldly. Underneath, in smaller letters, it revealed that this site was in the process of being excavated—in a scheme sponsored by the local Council and funded by a Government Commission; and that the two-year project was already half-way completed. Anyone interested enough to read on would be further informed that the remains of a substantial dwelling of the late Roman period was being gradually uncovered.

At the very end, in microscopic print, came the fact that this research was being carried out under the direction of a certain Miss Josephine Barnes, M.A., who had been specially invited over from her post at Cambridge University to supervise the work and co-

ordinate the team of unemployed young people actually
doing the digging.

This fresh April morning Miss Josephine Barnes,
M.A., had the place to herself, which was a welcome
relief. It was Sunday, but she knew her solitude was not
destined to last. Later in the morning, some of her
faithful team would be bound to arrive. They always
did, even at weekends when there was no need. She
suspected they had nothing better to do; also that they
were not able to tear themselves away from whatever
piece of ground they had left half-explored.

Just a year ago, they had come to her: complete
novices in the trade, and mostly with an attitude to
work in general which verged on the nihilistic. But over
the months, as she had worked with them, their
imaginations had been gripped by this tangible link
with their own past. It might be slow, painstaking
work—carefully sifting over each tiny patch of earth;
but the thrill of being first to find evidence of human
occupation all those centuries ago had given their
young lives a new dimension. It had given Josie a new
angle on things too, watching them. The idea of turning
disillusioned youngsters into budding archaeologists
made the whole project even more worthwhile than it
already was.

And they would not be the only ones who were
bound to roll up as the morning wore on. No doubt
they would be joined by the usual contingent of keen
local residents who enjoyed mucking in at weekends. Of
course she had to keep a close eye on their helpful
efforts: a heavy hand on the trowel could do more harm
than good. But Josie hated to discourage anyone who
showed a real interest in her subject. After all, it was
their village, and the scheme was funded from public
money. In a way they had a right to be there—a right
which she respected, even if it did add to her burden of
work rather than lighten it.

Now the results of almost a year's hard work lay

neatly labelled, drawn and exhibited in the Portacabin which had been set up next to her own caravan. Then there was the second caravan into which the workers could retire for warmth, shelter, a rest or a wash. Despite its rewards, she was the first to admit that digging could be a grimy and exhausting business.

Gazing round the site this morning, she knew there was every reason to feel proud. It was going well. They were ahead of schedule; two years, she had predicted, and she was confident that another year would see them through. She knew her trade, it was her life.

A smile of satisfaction lit her delicate features: the alert green eyes; the shapely expressive mouth; the small defiant chin; the tilted freckled nose. At the same moment a shaft of early sunlight reached out to touch her mane of soft curls, picking out gold among the gleaming russet, creating a halo effect of fiery red.

Her smile widened. The strengthening sun meant the end of winter, and even more intensive application to the job in hand. Josephine Barnes, M.A., was nothing if not single-minded—combining a rare intelligence with all the quick-tempered determination of her Irish forbears. Until this scheme was completed, she'd give her all to it. Nothing else would matter in her life. Nothing really did, except work, and that included other people—men, for example, who occasionally got notions of worming their way into her well-structured private world. They never stood a chance. Josie Barnes kept her priorities firmly under control.

Not that she was averse to a brief fling now and then between projects. She was a mature young woman of twenty-five, after all, and not made of stone. But they were just a recreation, a relaxation before embarking on the next serious enterprise. Among her colleagues she had developed a reputation for toughness, both of head and heart. This suited her fine; she made no attempt to disprove it but wore it wherever she went, whatever she did—like an outer garment, invisible chain mail. She had her reasons for steering clear of the male half of the human race; but she found them amusing enough as companions from time to time, and was far too realistic to deny the needs of her own body.

She basked a few minutes longer now, leaning against the door-frame of her temporary home, a trim figure in faded denims and an emerald sweater which covered all but the neat collar and cuffs of a pale blue cotton shirt. Then she gave herself a physical shake, glanced at her watch and turned to go in. The day was well under way. It was time to find some breakfast. This idling would never do.

But before she was through the door, her attention was caught by the swish of heavy tyres on mud, the throb of a powerful engine. She swung round—in time to see a small Japanese four-wheel-drive jeep—in bright orange—pulling off the dirt track beside her own faithful green Citroen *Deux-Cheveux*. She stared at it, brows knitted. Did she know anyone who owned such a rugged machine, or such a distinctive one? Let alone anyone likely to be bringing it here on a Sunday morning? It was too early yet for the weekend digging squad, and none of her team was in this vehicle's league, that was for sure.

She watched, overcome with curiosity, as the tall shape of a well-built man stepped down from the driving seat, slammed the door shut and strode over to read the notice. Even from this distance, his demeanour exuded dominance and strength, and she resisted an irrational urge to escape into the safe confines of her caravan where he couldn't see her. It was her responsibility, after all, to check up on everyone and anyone who came to the site. So she stayed where she was, seeing it through.

Screwing up her green eyes against the glare of the sun, she could just make out thick dark hair, a dark beard; black cord jeans and a chunky Aran sweater; tough, expensive boots. Suddenly, briskly, he finished his perusal of the notice and turned on his heel to march through the gate and straight towards her.

It was too late now even to consider escape. He had seen her, and his whole body shouted of purpose. So she stood her ground—arms calmly folded, expression composed—as he approached. As soon as he was close enough to come into focus, she was clearly aware of deep brown eyes—warm but intense, sharp on her face and form—studying every detail of her with barely a flicker while his steady pace never faltered. She allowed her own lucid green gaze to return the inspection, cool beneath long auburn lashes.

Her quick mind was busy making its inventory, filing its report. He was around thirty, it decided: a tanned outdoor freshness to his skin, a springing energy in his step; but on closer scrutiny there was a conflicting air of thoughtfulness and introspection about him. Those profound penetrating eyes; the firm, sensitive mouth framed by the neatly curling dark beard, which did nothing to disguise the square thrust of the chin; the long, faintly aquiline nose; the trace of a frown furrowing the high brow over which the almost black hair fell with a life of its own . . . no, it wasn't going to be easy to pin a label on this one, she thought. Shrewd enough to be an academic; muscular enough to be a farmer. Josie was a firm believer in her own judgment, and in first impressions, but in this case her first impression was so overwhelmingly forceful that it was incredibly difficult to reach any rational conclusion about him at all.

So she waited in silence—letting him make the first move, the first contact, regarding him solemnly as his long strides shortened and halted at the foot of her steps. For a moment or two he stood, one boot on the lowest step, hands in pockets, returning her calm gaze with a kind of friendly insolence. Then, quite suddenly, he smiled. Uneven, sincere, the smile brought crinkles to the corners of his eyes—and an unusually instant reflex response from Josie. It was not the sort of smile you could easily fail to return. It took even her defences by surprise.

'Good morning.' The voice was pleasant, deep, deliberate.

'What can I do for you?' Josie had never been one to waste time on meaningless social niceties. She liked to think that bluntness was one of her trade marks.

The heavy, near-black brows lifted sardonically, as if he was tempted to give her an equally direct reply— quite possibly in dubious taste. One corner of his mouth twitched upwards in suppressed amusement. But all he said was, 'Is Miss Barnes about, by any chance?'

Josie's eyes narrowed in suspicion. Who was he, and why was he here looking for her on a Sunday morning? 'About what?' she hedged cautiously.

He laughed outright, showing very white, strong teeth. 'About her business, I suppose. Whatever it is high-powered lady archaeologists do on fine spring mornings when not busy directing important excavations.' Head on one side, eyes narrowed, he intensified his assessment of her. 'Are you one of her team?' he hazarded.

She unfolded her arms and shoved her hands into the pockets of her jeans, drawing herself up to her full five foot two, taking advantage of the fact that she was four steps above him to glare fiercely down into his face. 'As a matter of fact,' she informed him haughtily, 'I am Josephine Barnes. You need look no further. And now that you've located me,' she repeated laboriously, 'what can I do for you?'

Once again the heavy eyebrows rose to meet the dark hair. He took a step back, broad thumbs hooked into his belt. His tone registered renewed interest—and more than a hint of surprise. 'Miss Josephine Barnes, M.A., Cantab., director of the Summerford Archaeological Project, author of a number of learned treatises on the subject of late Romano-British settlements, with particular reference to the use of sandstone and limestone in residential and agricultural constructions?'

She nodded gravely. 'The very same.'

'Authority on the methods and materials employed in the manufacture of mosaics and concrete floorings?' he persisted half-serious, half-satirical.

It was her turn to raise her eyebrows. Whoever he was, he had obviously been doing some homework. 'That's right,' she confirmed coolly, playing for time. '*Tesserae* and *Opus Signinum*. So, now that we've sorted all that out, perhaps you'll tell me what it was you actually wanted?'

For a moment, a mask seemed to settle across the open features. His air of jaunty irony became overlaid with something veiled and speculative, but his smile was no less warm. 'Oh, nothing really. Just to introduce myself—meet the mastermind behind all this.' He stepped on to the lowest rung again, right hand outstretched. Josie reached down in order to shake it with her own, his grasp was firm and enveloping. 'Alex Grant,' he told her succinctly. 'I've read some of your papers. Fascinating.' The dark eyes glinted. 'Somehow,' he added pensively, 'I hadn't imagined you quite like this.'

'Oh?' In spite of herself, she could not resist the obvious question. 'How did you imagine me, then?'

He dropped her hand, after clasping it several seconds longer than strictly necessary. 'Well, with your reputation for academic distinction and serious dedication, I suppose I'd envisaged you older, drier . . . more . . .'

'More of a desiccated middle-aged spinster?' she supplied caustically.

'Hardly that,' he grinned. 'But perhaps more imposing, austere, than you appear to be,' he suggested carefully, the soul of tact.

Josie was quite unable to decide whether to take this as an insult or a compliment, so she took refuge in folding her arms again and surveying him solemnly. 'Well, as you see,' she remarked, 'I'm a perfectly ordinary person, doing a perfectly ordinary job of work.'

His denial was instant and vehement. 'Oh no, I beg to differ. Not ordinary, Miss Barnes. No way.' The sentiment was straightforward enough—but there was something almost threatening about the terse, emphatic phrases, about the way his dark eyes assessed her as he spoke.

Josie cleared her throat. It was high time they got down to business—whatever that might be. 'Perhaps, Mr Grant,' she invited in her most clipped tones, 'you'd just like to tell me why you're here. Were you just passing by or was there actually some reason for honouring me with this visit?'

'I did have a reason, yes. In a way,' he explained cryptically, 'we're in the same trade, you and I.'

'You mean you're an archaeologist?' She frowned, searching her memory. She rarely forgot a name nor a face—and she was unlikely, her mind suggested cynically, to have forgotten one like this. 'I don't think I've heard your . . .'

'Not exactly,' he interrupted, even more mysteriously. He grinned, enjoying her perplexity, then he thrust his hands into his pockets.

'Mr Grant.' She was rapidly losing patience, her tone laced with exasperation. 'I haven't got time for riddles. Either tell me why you're here, or . . .'

'Okay, okay.' He held up both hands as if fending her off. Then, unrepentant, he provided her with another clue. 'We're both concerned with human dwellings, but in different time-scales. You like to know how the ancients constructed their homes; I have to decide how we should build ours.' He watched her, waiting for the penny to drop.

It already had. 'An architect!'

He inclined his head graciously. 'Full marks, Miss

Barnes. So you see,' he pointed out persuasively, 'we have common ground. A shared interest, wouldn't you say?'

Josie pursed up her mouth sceptically. 'I hadn't given it much thought, Mr Grant,' she assured him truthfully. 'In any case it doesn't explain why you're here. Unless you decided to take a few tips from your long-dead colleagues?' she suggested, her gaze level, her tone wry.

'Something like that.' Beneath the charming exterior he was cagey, almost as cautious as she was herself. Whatever it was he had come looking for she sensed he was becoming increasingly reluctant to tell her about it. 'How about showing me round,' he continued, 'if you've got a few minutes to spare? Or if you'd rather,' he added blandly, 'I could stroll round on my own, and then come back and have a word with you? I did rather want to talk to you,' he admitted, more confusingly than ever.

Josie hadn't had any breakfast and acute curiosity was clashing painfully with an urgent need for a cup of coffee. She was not in the habit of allowing total strangers to poke about her precious site without close supervision. On the other hand . . .

She made up her mind quickly and without hesitation, as usual. 'Look, I'll tell you what. I was about to make myself some coffee. Will you come in and join me, then you can say what you came to say? After that, if you still want to, we can look round. I'm expecting the first weekend diggers in . . .' she consulted her watch, 'an hour or so—so if we could . . .'

'That would be delightful.' Again, that spicing of humour beneath the formality.

Turning, she led the way into her tiny home. He took the four stairs in two easy strides, ducking his dark head as he fitted his frame through the small doorway, once inside it dwarfed the compact room. 'Charming,' he murmured politely, his sharp gaze taking in the orderly miniature scene of bright curtains, neat bunks, folding table, diminutive wardrobe and cupboards and shelves stacked with papers and books.

'It's just a caravan,' she retorted roundly. Then she flashed him one of her rare wide smiles. 'For God's sake,' she urged, 'sit down. You make it feel like a wendy house!'

He glanced round again and, in the absence of a chair, he sprawled across one of the narrow bunks. Josie turned her back on him, busying herself with the little bottle-gas stove, filling the kettle from the one cold tap. Feeling those eyes upon her she stifled an acute unaccustomed embarrassment. She was well-used to visitors—of either sex—making themselves at home around her; but there was something disconcerting about the way Alex Grant was dominating the confined space.

'I usually eat in the other van,' she explained, taking two mugs from the low dresser and spooning instant coffee granules into them. 'I'm not kitted out for more than drinks and snacks in here.' Unable to find anything else to do, she turned to face him.

He was calm and relaxed, as if he spent every day partaking of mugs of coffee in small caravans with lady archaeologists. Not, her mind reflected, a man who would be easy to perturb. 'It's very cosy,' he said pleasantly. 'And I should think it needs to be. Surely Miss Barnes, you haven't been here all winter?' he enquired.

'Why not?' she countered indignantly, sensing a challenge. 'Not much point in taking on a job if you desert it at the first sign of frost.' Lesser mortals, her tone clearly implied, might do just that, but not Josephine Barnes, M.A.

'Hmmm.' He was gazing at her thoughtfully. 'You must be tougher than you look.'

Once again he was playing at enigmatic compliments. There was no answer to this one either, so she turned round to pour out the boiling water. 'Milk? Sugar?'

'Both, thanks.' She handed him his coffee, set an open tin of digestive biscuits on the table, and sat down on the bunk opposite him, clasping her fingers round her own steaming cup. Then, munching one of the biscuits, she lifted her sea-green eyes to his face. 'Right,' she demanded briskly. 'What's this all about?'

He sipped his coffee, helping himself to a biscuit. There was no doubt about it—he was in no hurry to enlighten her. In fact, he was quite definitely stalling. 'Nothing if not direct, are you, Miss Josephine Barnes?'

She ignored the teasing, the slight mockery, in the question. 'I prefer to know where I stand, yes. Get down to facts. So, if you'd . . .'

'Facts, eh?' he cut in, his expression quizzical, the brown eyes warm on her face. 'Brass tacks? Not much room in your packed schedule for mystery or fantasy or uncertainty?' He paused, and, as she groped for a reply to this unexpected accusation, he pressed on even more mischievously, 'And what about feelings, Miss Barnes? Or are they taboo?'

Even Josie's close friends, of whom there were few, rarely allowed themselves to make such personal observations as this. His insolent conjecture was sharply, and uncomfortably accurate, but she kept her reaction concealed. She had had plenty of practice at controlling anything resembling true feelings. He was right.

'I don't see that it's any concern of yours, Mr Grant.' Her voice was cold now, her gaze unflinching. 'And I'm a busy woman. So if you wouldn't mind . . .'

Yet again, in his nonchalant way, he cut her off before she could demand an explanation of his presence there. 'Can't we get past all this "Mr Grant" business? The name,' he reminded her kindly, 'is Alex. Or, if you persist in clinging to the formalities, Alexander.'

He was teasing her now. Josie had always detested being teased, and this time was no exception. 'All right then—Alex,' she conceded stiffly. 'But I still want to know . . .'

'Patience—Josephine.' Tentatively he tried out her first name. It sounded alien, unfamiliar, on his lips. 'I'm coming to that, now that we're through the introductions. Boring things, I always think, introductions. Don't you?'

'Josie,' she muttered reluctantly, accepting a defeat she could scarcely define.

'Josie.' He repeated it, twice, relishing its sound, turning it over on his tongue. 'That's nice—very nice. I like it. A lively, lovely name; it suits you,' he announced, disarming in his sincerity.

At this rate he would have her blushing, and she never, ever, did that any more. She had not done it for years—just as she had not wept, or permitted herself any of those other weak, childish, emotional lapses. Not for years; she had almost lost count of the years—ten, eleven? Not since she grew up, not gradually, gently, through the normal trials of adolescence—but all at once, in one devastating blow. Not since . . .

'Now look here, Mr Grant . . . Alex.' Firmly, she took the situation in hand. 'I don't know why you're here, or what your game is. But I really have got a lot to see to; the public will be here soon, and probably some of my team too. I'm sure you have an excellent reason for this call, but if you don't tell me what it is—now, this minute—I'm going to get on with my work and leave you to see yourself off the premises, when you're ready.' And she set her empty mug down on the formica table-top with a loud, positive, final *clunk*.

Without batting an eyelid, Alex drained the last of his coffee and put his cup beside hers. Then he stood up, instantly reducing everything once again to doll's house size. 'Absolutely right, Josie.' His easy-going acceptance of her reproach was far more disconcerting than an equal irritation would have been. 'I'm a dreamer, no sense of urgency, all my friends will tell you. A hopeless case. Come on,' he pleaded winningly. 'Show me round—you said you would. I want to see everything.'

Seeing her hesitation, he turned up both palms and spread his fingers in a gesture of mock-appeal. 'Please, Josie? I'll tell you why I'm here as we go,' he promised, baiting the hook.

She flashed him a glance of pure annoyance; but she grabbed a jacket and marched ahead of him out of the caravan—unaccountably relieved to escape from its suddenly claustrophobic confines. Grinning he followed, remembering just in time to bend as he came to the low door.

As she led Alex round the site, pointing out lines of stone wall here, fragments of floor or roofing slab there, describing their treasured finds which indicated almost constant occupation of the plot from prehistoric times right through to the fifth century, Josie began to relax, even to enjoy herself. She was in her element; and he was a receptive, intelligent audience. If there was one thing that could pierce Josie's barriers, it was an avid listener as she shared her life's obsession.

She paused beside a pair of low masonry walls at one corner of the field. 'And this,' she told him proudly, 'was what started it all off.'

'The corn-drying oven?' Immediately the words were out he became blank, impassive, almost as if he was disowning them.

Her glance was sharp. 'You know more about this than you've been letting on,' she accused.

'Everyone knows it was the Roman oven the builders first stumbled across.' His manner was defensive, the mask had fallen again. She regarded him curiously, but she let him continue—waiting to see how much he would give away. 'I live and work locally—in Bath—and it was in all the papers.' Rather feverishly, he emphasised his case. 'How the builders were just starting on the footings of the new development here, and they unearthed these walls, and the architect thought it might be important, so the firm halted work while they found out.'

She was still watching him closely, a suspicion setting firm in her mind. He was quite right, of course, that was exactly what had happened, some fifteen months ago, but his expression wasn't quite straightforward. There was something—she could have sworn—almost furtive about the look in his eyes.

'Well,' she said slowly, her gaze steady on his face, 'that architect was most enlightened. If he hadn't decided to call a halt to the work, we might never have known all this was here. A major archaeological discovery would never have been made. Whoever he is,' she added, studying him from under her lashes, 'we in the trade owe him a great deal. I forget his name— perhaps you know him?' she suggested, all airy innocence, her eyes sparkling.

He grinned, then hung his head penitently. 'Rumbled! Exposed!' He held his hand to his brow, overcome with satirical remorse. 'Your wit has penetrated my true identity. Forgive me, Miss Barnes,' he held out one hand beseechingly, 'for attempting to deceive you?'

She folded her arms and shook her head sternly, then she returned the grin. 'What was your surname . . . Grant? Of course!' The green eyes widened in recollection. 'I knew I'd seen it somewhere . . . what was it . . .' she frowned, struggling to envisage the three names at the top of the plans she had once been shown, way back at the start of the dig. 'Grant . . . Randle . . . and who was the third? Holt—that was it—Grant Randle Holt. Dynamic young team, I was informed at the time. Top firm in the area.' She chuckled. 'No wonder you're so interested in the place.'

His remorse had given way to a fleeting surprise at her reaction, and then he regained his usual air of amused directness. 'Got it in two. Flattering of you to remember.'

'Eventually,' she criticised herself wrily. 'I should've remembered long before that—or guessed at least. I must be slipping. Why didn't you simply tell me who you were, straight out?' she demanded, serious now. 'Why all the mystery?'

He looked down, kicking gently at a clump of grass—equally solemn suddenly. Josie sensed a shiver of foreboding, an inexplicable anxiety passing subtly between them, almost tangible on the bright morning air. 'I don't know.' He was still stalling, even now, she could swear it. 'I had the feeling you might not approve of the man responsible for designing all those new houses due to cover up your hard work. I did my best to see that they harmonised with the countryside, blended with nature and all that ... but the fact remains, they're ultra-modern, and they're going to go up, right here.'

'But not till we've completed our excavations,' she pointed out, astonished at the awkward apology in his tone. 'We archaeologists are quite used to having to fit our activities in around twentieth-century developments. It's not the first time I've supervised a dig while a firm of builders kicked their heels, waiting for us to get out of their way.'

'I'm glad you take it so ... philosophically,' he said simply.

'Anyway,' she warmed to her subject, 'it's the actual developers who influence these decisions not their architects. I could hardly have held you responsible for Wallace Holdings. And they've been pretty decent, really, they gave us the full time I specified after they called me in. Two years, I said. Once we've dug every inch over, made careful diagrams and stowed all the relics away safely in their museums and vaults—well,' she shrugged, 'the actual site's done its work. We can all go home.'

'Funny thing.' His glance was acute. 'I've been assuming you'd hate the idea of brand new, space-age houses sprawling all over your ancient site. That's why I've kept out of your way all this time—though I was intrigued to see what was going on. I suppose I thought you'd find my presence needling ... insulting.'

She laughed at such a whimsical notion. 'I can't afford such spurious sentimentality, Alex. I love the rural scene as much as the next person; but people have to live somewhere—and it's right on the edge of a village, after all. It doesn't do to get too attached to a place in my experience,' she added, her tone dry. 'You get what you can and then move on.'

The dark eyes were very shrewd, quizzical, as they flickered across her face. 'As long as you don't apply that policy to people?' he commented quietly.

She ignored this, evading his gaze, transferring her own to the middle distance. 'I seem to remember,' she went on firmly as if he had not spoken, 'that it was a superbly-planned estate. Beautiful proportions, land-scaped gardens, every possible comfort—solar heating and all, if I'm not mistaken?'

His tone came down-to-earth to match hers. 'Correct. Nothing but the best for Wallace Holdings' up-market developments . . . solar panels, extensive roof, wall and floor insulation, full double glazing, skirting-level radiation . . .' Sardonically, as if reciting from a brochure, he checked these desirable attributes off on his fingers.

'Of course, you realise you're two thousand years or so behind with the full central heating bit?' Glad to be on safer ground, she waved a hand around the field. 'The Romans knew all about that. Even this settlement had its hypocaust—and it wasn't a particularly up-market villa, or anything like that.' She grinned.

'I know. The original under-floor duct system.' After a slight pause, he took a step back, his glance sweeping over her whole figure now with warm approval. 'I must say, Miss Josephine Barnes, M.A., you've turned out to be quite a surprise. I'm rather glad I took the plunge and dropped by. I'm not sure what I expected . . .'

'A five-thousand-year-old, solid flint battle-axe, perhaps?' she offered, poker-faced, refusing to show her response to his honest scrutiny.

'Whatever it was, you've confounded my fears,' he repeated gravely. 'I wish I'd come earlier now, instead of keeping a tactfully low profile.'

'We're pretty reasonable on the whole, as I said, we digging fraternity,' she assured him lightly. 'As long as we're given space and time to manoeuvre. Just leave us in peace to achieve what we set out to do, allow us the paltry sums that are usually at our disposal, and we'll hardly complain at all.'

'Yes, well.' Again she was sure she caught that brief hardening of the mouth, the veiling of the eyes as he looked away. 'I think I've seen it all now. I'll just have a quick look at the exhibits—presumably you've got them locked up in the cabin?'

'That's right.' Her gaze followed his to the corner of the field and outside the fence, where a small procession of invaders now loped along the track. Some on foot, some on bikes, they were a motley crew, ranging from the conventional to the outlandish. As they came nearer, a strange assortment of outfits could be discerned—not to mention hair sculpted into garish styles and shades.

Josie sent them a cheery wave of welcome, which they returned enthusiastically. 'Here come my faithful helpers. They're early today—they've arrived before the village contingent. They'll be delighted to display some of their discoveries to you, if you play your cards right.' She smiled over at them.

'You sound almost affectionate.' He stared at them dubiously.

'Why not?' she countered at once, defensive as a mother hen with her brood. 'They're great kids, and hard workers. Some of them haven't had much of a life so far—but they're coming on wonderfully now. Give me another year,' she went on firmly, 'and I'll really make something out of some of these punks and rockers you see wending their way towards you. As well as using all that youthful energy to collect enough material for a thoroughly comprehensive survey—one of the best I've ever done. So there!'

She swung round to confront him, the light of challenge in her eyes—but he was already striding away in the direction of the caravans. For a few seconds she watched his powerful back receding into the distance. Forceful and striking he might be—warm and sensitive too, no doubt—but after all, he was only a man. And men, as she knew, were notoriously fickle creatures. Unpredictable, even the best of them; prone to inconsistent shifts of mood and attitude.

Shrugging philosophically, she set off across the field after him.

CHAPTER TWO

HE was still there two hours later. Josie's young trainees
had been closely followed by several members of the
public, and she was soon enmeshed in supervising their
activities. Her assistants particularly enjoyed their role
as hosts and teachers to the weekend amateurs; some of
them had become quite good at it, adopting an air of
slightly patronising expertise which made Josie smile to
herself. She suspected that was the main reason why
they kept turning up when they had no need to.

Whenever she had a moment to glance round, Alex
was involved somewhere on the site—chatting ani-
matedly to one of her helpers or a local resident;
peering with intelligent curiosity into some part of their
discoveries; or, on one occasion, simply standing alone
at a far corner of the field, apparently lost in
contemplation as he stared over at the hive of industry
going on there.

Probably only imagining what it would be like once
his own brain-child covered the area, the cynical half of
Josie's mind taunted sarcastically. She still found herself
faintly puzzled to understand why he had suddenly
taken it into his head to investigate the dig. In her
opinion, his claim to objective interest did not ring quite
true. *Methinks*, her mind harped sceptically, *the
gentleman doth protest too much*. Whatever his
motivations, she was far too busy just now to stop and
work them out.

By one o'clock the crowd had thinned out
considerably. Some of her team had brought picnics,
and now retired importantly to their private caravan to
brew up the perennial tea. Everyone else had meals
waiting for them at home. The Sunday dinner ritual

must never be interrupted, Josie knew, whatever the distraction.

She straightened up from her own work, picking up her green sweater from where it lay discarded on the ground. Without the sharp wind which so often chilled this exposed site, it had become quite a warm day. Slim and supple as a cat, she stretched herself out towards the sun's rays. The caress of them felt magical on her skin—almost sinful, after the long bleak winter. Closing her eyes she turned her face up to them, pushing back the stray curls which had fallen across it, soft strands, now burnished to a rich chestnut.

'There's a stirring sight!'

How long had he been standing so close behind her? Alex Grant—she had forgotten all about him for a few minutes. For no good reason at all she felt annoyed with herself. For even less reason, she felt irritated with him.

She whirled round to confront him. As before, his smile reached his eyes, imparting a genuine warmth—spiced, at this moment, with blatant appreciation. 'So—you're still with us, are you?' The rhetorical question was all she could come up with to cover her temporary confusion.

'As you see,' he agreed pleasantly.

'I'm sorry I couldn't spend any longer showing you round.' She mustered her dignity, became all brisk efficiency. 'I've been rather occupied.'

'So I noticed,' he remarked. 'A lady much in demand. Is it always like this?'

'Oh no. Hardly anyone came at all in the winter. But once summer really gets under way, I expect it'll be even worse!' She sighed, affecting bored weariness as she gazed round the now peaceful field. 'I hate to discourage them, they do love it!'

'And so do you, Josie,' he challenged, grinning. 'You love every minute of it—including being invaded by all these eager beavers, you know you do.'

'Maybe.' She stared past him, wishing those dark eyes wouldn't give the impression they were penetrating to the inside of her head. 'Did you see all you wanted to see?'

'And more. I'm most impressed: your young associates did a great job of showing off the exhibits. They're a credit to you, those kids. I can quite see what you meant about their enthusiasm—it's infectious.' He chuckled. 'And quite incongruous in a few cases. Taught me a lesson in not taking people at their face value, I must say,' he added ruefully.

Despite her caution, she had to warm to him: the way he made no bones about criticising himself; his unreserved praise of her own efforts. 'I told you,' she reminded him, 'between us, those youngsters and me, we'll make something of this project we can all be proud of by the end of another year.'

His gaze left her face—abruptly, it seemed to her—and narrowed on to the green horizon. Then he was launching into action—glancing at his watch, running a firm hand through his thick hair, apparently bringing himself into line. 'This will never do—I've got to be off. I was expected to lunch ten minutes ago. They'll kill me!'

'Don't let me detain you,' she said politely, tensing herself to ignore the uncomfortable message which nagged behind his words. Why shouldn't he be expected home for lunch? It was perfectly normal.

'Would you mind very much,' he was asking now, 'if I came back later and brought them with me? I'd really like to show them all this—and I promise to keep the little ones under control.'

'Not at all. We have plenty of children coming along, as you saw.' It was a struggle to keep her voice cool and steady. There was no reason on earth why he should not have a family. Even less reason why she should be so taken aback at the idea.

'Great—I'll see you in a couple of hours, then? Enjoy

your break—I'm sure you need it.' Without wasting time on further trivialities, he was gone, a man of speedy decisions, speedier actions.

She watched him climb into the square, solid Daihatsu and roar off along the road. Then she drew in a few deep breaths before joining her team in the van for a snack. They would expect her to be her usual sociable, relaxed self—and there was no way she was going to let them down. There were enough let-downs in life without her adding to them.

In the afternoon she was even busier. The sun shone, attracting more families than ever to the dig. Bustling about, making sure everyone was safely occupied and that no one trod on any particularly delicate patches or tripped over any submerged foundations, Josie almost forgot all about her impending visit from Alex Grant and his tribe.

Almost, but not quite. She was conscious of being on edge the whole time; even when she forgot what it was she was waiting for, she knew she was expecting something. Like the niggling awareness of a discomfort due to be faced, the looming knowledge of a trip to the dentist the next day.

She happened to be looking up when they arrived. The line of vehicles outside the fence now stretched quite a way up the track, and the large estate car had to park some distance from the gate. Determined not to appear too interested, she applied herself assiduously to what she was doing; but covertly she glanced round to see who would get out of it.

Alex was the first to leave the car—from the passenger seat. He reached into the back and emerged with a small blond child, which he lifted on to his broad shoulders with practised ease. It bounced gleefully up and down as he strode over to the gate, waving its small hands in delight.

Josie turned away, an unaccountable constriction in her throat. Then curiosity gained the upper hand, and she looked back again. A plump young woman had got out of the driving seat and was fussing around two equally blond older children—making sure they had their boots on, locking their shoes away in the car. Then the three of them walked behind Alex into the field.

As they approached, Josie became deeply absorbed in her task, and when Alex appeared, greeting her with a friendly 'hallo again!' she was able to jump quite convincingly.

She smiled as naturally as possible. 'Enjoy your lunch?'

He turned to grin at the woman who was catching up with him, and she grinned back. It was a familiar glance, Josie thought—intimate, sideways, knowing—exchanged between two people who had been close for a long time. 'It wasn't too dried up,' he told her. 'I didn't get my knuckles rapped too hard.'

'I'm sure you didn't.' For a moment Josie felt awkward. She glanced at the woman—and found herself confronting an open, honest face. The eyes, very sharp and blue, smiled without reserve into hers; the hair, as straight and fair as her children's, was cut short to frame regular features that were well-made rather than beautiful.

'Josie—meet Vicky,' Alex introduced—as usual without ceremony. The two women nodded to each other. 'I've told Vicky all about you,' he informed Josie. 'Nothing but good, I assure you,' he added, his eyes gleaming, as she regarded him uncertainly.

'I can't wait to see what you're up to here.' Vicky's voice was as pleasant as her expression. 'It sounds really exciting.'

Conflicting instincts were creating a brief tension in Josie. This was a person she could like quite a lot, she sensed that at once, and yet, as Alex's wife, she set off twinges of resentment—whether Josie acknowledged it or not. 'You're very welcome,' she said, and then felt slightly stupid. 'I mean—please feel free to look round, I'm rather inundated this afternoon, but I'm sure one of my team will show you—or perhaps Alex is expert enough by now to take you round himself?' she suggested, with more than a touch of irony.

The other woman didn't appear to notice the wry note. 'Thanks—I'd like that. But don't put yourself out, Josie. We'll nose about—we'll be very careful, and I'll keep the kids out of your way.'

The smallest child was now wriggling on his high perch, demanding to be put down. The other two stood close to their mother, staring at Josie from remarkably similar blue eyes. They certainly did not take after Alex physically, she reflected—and immediately wished she hadn't. The passing thought was distinctly needling. 'They won't be any trouble,' she said, smiling at them. She had not had a lot of experience with children, but she liked them, and these examples of the species seemed perfectly civilised—as she might have expected any offspring of Alex's to be. 'Just keep out of the marked-off areas. Ask one of us if you're not sure.'

Alex had set the complaining bundle gently on the ground; at once the child made a beeline for his mother, hugging her bejeaned legs, glancing round at Josie and then burying his face again. Vicky reached down to stroke the small, shining head. 'This is Matthew. He isn't really as shy as he pretends to be.'

'And this,' Alex indicated the oldest child, 'is Rachel and this is Emily.' He put one arm round each of the girls: proud, proprietorial.

'Hallo, Rachel and Emily—and Matthew.' Josie welcomed them all solemnly.

Shyly, the two girls echoed her greeting. 'I've got new wellies,' Matthew declared fiercely, still muffled against his mother's knees.

Josie inspected the bright blue rubber boots. 'You certainly have. They're much nicer than mine.'

He risked a quick glance at her feet. 'You aren't wearing any!' he exploded, deeply offended.

'No, because it's not very wet today. But I've got some, and I often wear them,' she assured him earnestly.

'Where are they?' he demanded dubiously.

'In my caravan—over there.'

'What colour are they?' Gripped by this exciting topic, he very nearly forgot to hold on to his mother.

'Black.'

'Do you live in the caravan all the time?' Rachel ventured. She was a pretty child of about seven, Josie supposed.

'At the moment, yes.'

'You lucky thing!' Rachel sighed deeply. 'It must be super—I wish I did.'

'Jolly cold, I should think, in winter,' Vicky reminded her daughter practically.

'Not everyone would like it,' Josie admitted, 'but I do.'

'Don't you get lonely, all by yourself?' Rachel's reserve was melting away in the reflected glow of Josie's romantic lifestyle.

Alex had been standing slightly to one side, following this conversation with detached amusement. 'What makes you so sure that she lives all by herself?' The question was aimed at Rachel, but his eyes were on Josie.

Rachel could find no answer to it, and she was much too shy to ask, so she just stared at Josie in round-eyed admiration. Emily, the middle child, was clearly less of a dreamer. 'I'd rather live in a proper house,' she announced. 'Caravans are only for holidays.'

Vicky laughed. 'Emily likes her creature comforts. Come on, you lot,' she shepherded her brood together. 'Josie's got a lot to do, she doesn't want us cluttering up her field for too long. If we could just have a quick look?' She smiled at Josie again. 'I know the children would like to see the exhibits—and I'd like to see everything.'

'Don't bother to come with us,' Alex said. 'After your detailed tuition this morning, I should be able to deliver a full lecture on the subject.'

'I think,' Josie returned brusquely, 'you'll find two of my helpers in the Portacabin, ready to tell you anything you want to know.' Somehow this morning seemed a long time ago. She turned to Vicky. 'As I said, please feel free to wander around. But you must excuse me now—I ought to be making sure all the other ... sightseers are okay.'

Out of the corner of her eye, she glimpsed Alex's heavy brows lifting—registering ironic surprise at being lumped in with all those other weekenders. But after all, she thought—walking away quickly about her business— that was all they were, just another family come to kill an empty Sunday under her auspices. A very pleasant family, too. Nothing to feel irritated about.

Half an hour later, just as she had finished explaining the corn-drying oven to some visitors, she came face-to-face with Vicky, who had been standing unobtrusively on the fringes of the group.

'Amazing.' Vicky had been watching and listening intently. 'It must have been a wonderful moment when you first realised the full extent of what you had here.' Her own countenance lit up as she imagined it.

'It was.' Almost unconsciously, Josie's glance ranged around and behind the other woman, searching for her companions.

Vicky noticed at once. 'They're still looking at the exhibits. Your trainees are marvellous—you've done a wonderful job with them.'

'I'm glad they're making themselves useful.' Josie tried to keep the tautness from her voice—Vicky was altogether too perceptive for her liking.

'One of them even took Matthew out of the way and entertained him while we had a better look.' Vicky grinned. 'He can be such a handful. Alex is good with him, but it was a relief to have five minutes without his constant demands.'

Well of course, Alex would be good with him. After all, he was the boy's father. 'They're lovely children,' Josie said stiffly. She meant it, but she found it hard to relax with Vicky. 'Very like you,' she added, 'especially in colouring.'

'Well, of course we're both very fair—their father and myself,' came the totally bewildering reply. 'I suppose they were bound to turn out that way.' She was obviously quite unaware of the profound effect her simple remark was having on her audience.

'Their father?' Josie fought to contain her reaction as shock gave way to disbelief. 'But I thought . . .'

Vicky stared at her for a moment, picking up the tightness in her voice in spite of her valiant efforts to control it. 'Yes, their father—my husband, John. He's as blond as the rest of us.' She frowned, and then suddenly her features split into a broad grin. 'You don't mean . . . you didn't think. . . .' She broke off, covering her mouth with one hand.

'I thought Alex was their father. Your husband,' Josie emphasised, in case Vicky hadn't got the message. An odd feeling of elation was coursing through her which she preferred not to analyse.

Then they were both laughing, together; and Vicky's hand was on her arm in a gesture of easy friendship as they shared the joke. 'You mean to say,' she spluttered, 'that he didn't *tell* you who I was?'

'Not exactly.' Josie cast her mind back to the way the conversation had gone. 'He didn't say you were his family, but he didn't say you weren't. And when he tore off in such a hurry so as not to be late for lunch . . . well . . . I thought . . .'

'Of course you did!' Vicky was still giggling. 'Good Lord—fancy thinking we were all his brood! How hilarious! Wait till I tell him—and John. They'll fall about.'

'I dare say.' Josie had stopped laughing. There was something she did not quite like about the idea of Alex grinning at her mistake.

Vicky became serious too, and glanced sharply at her. 'On second thoughts,' she said blandly, 'I won't say anything, if you don't.'

'I won't,' Josie assured her vehemently. 'Thanks,' she added—grateful for the older woman's intuitive understanding of her feelings. 'I only met Alex for the first time today,' she reminded her. 'For all I knew, he might well have been a much-married man.'

'For all you still know,' Vicky observed with a mischievous twinkle, 'he might well be.' Then, catching Josie's expression, she went on quickly, 'But he isn't! As a matter of fact, he's one of the most eligible bachelors I know.' Again the sharp glance; uncomfortably, Josie looked away—but her ears were all attention. 'One of the most confirmed, too. Married to the job, we always tell him. Several women have thought they had him taped, over the years—but he won't be pinned down. A shameful waste of good husband material, if you ask me,' Vicky declared wickedly. 'He makes a lovely friend—and honorary uncle to the children. They adore him. He ought to have some of his own,' she concluded thoughtfully.

Josie decided it was time to move the subject on to more neutral ground. They were strolling round the edge of the field now, away from the crowds swarming over the central area. 'Is he a colleague of your husband's, then?'

'My husband,' Vicky informed her succinctly, 'is a writer. No, I'm the colleague.'

Josie stopped dead. '*You're* Alex's colleague? An architect?'

Vicky smiled pleasantly. 'Why not? You're an archaeologist. Can't I be an architect?'

Josie was annoyed with herself. This was turning out to be the day of the embarrassing confrontation. 'Of course you can. Of course. It was just that—with the children being so small—I hadn't stopped to think . . .'

'Don't worry.' Vicky patted her arm as they resumed their walk. 'You were bound to be surprised. Mind you,' she pointed out sardonically, 'if *you* react like that, imagine how the most dyed-in-the-wool chauvinist male takes that piece of information.' Josie winced, seeing what she meant. 'But I'm luckier than most,' Vicky explained. 'John writes thrillers—he's doing quite well—and so he's at home most of the time; and we have a wonderful girl who lives with us.'

'A nanny?' Josie suggested.

'I hate that word.' Vicky wrinkled up her nose. 'It doesn't seem to suit Annie at all.' She giggled. 'Annie the Nanny. No, just a—a mother's help, if you like. She's been with us since the girls were small and I went back to work full-time. Then my parents live round the corner—it's all very convenient, I hardly stopped work at all when I had Matthew. I went in with Alex four years ago—when he set the firm up. I love it,' she said simply.

'So . . .' Josie was slowly piecing it together. 'Are you Randle—or Holt?'

'Vicky Randle, at your service. If he'd been bothered to give me a surname in the first place, this confusion could have been avoided. Alex was never one for such formalities,' she mused. 'Hates anything pompous or irrelevant. That's why he gets on so well with John.'

Josie was becoming increasingly interested. 'So—who's Holt?'

'Julian's our third partner. Been with us about two years now. He's very young, trendy and dynamic—but Alex is the real flair, the imagination behind the outfit. I've got plenty of know-how—commonsense, you could say—but Alex is our core, our . . . flame. He's a brilliant planner and designer, and totally dedicated to the profession.'

'I caught a glimpse of the plans for this development

when I first took over the dig,' Josie recalled. 'I don't know much about these things, but it certainly looked attractive and professional.'

'Oh, it was that all right. Everything Alex does is professional—and it has the human touch. That's why Wallace Holdings wanted him on this job—they knew he was the best. Even when we were at college together, I knew Alex was going to go far. I'm lucky to be riding on his bandwaggon,' she confided, with disarming honesty. 'I was really studying landscape architecture so I take on most of the routine environmental work.'

'Is that why you wanted to look round here? You must have an interest in what's happening after we've finished with it?'

For a second, Josie could have sworn there was an echo of that expression she had caught earlier on Alex's face—guarded, cautious, then it was gone. 'That's right. I've already done lots of work on it, of course, when we drew up the original plans. But that was quite a time ago. We thought we should give ourselves a refresher course since there's been this delay. A few minor changes might have to be made after you've gone.'

Was there just a hint of anxiety under Vicky's confident, even tone? Josie could not be sure, so she dismissed the idea. 'Only another year or so,' she pointed out, 'and it'll be all yours again. We've got lots more to do yet, though, before we're ready to hand it back to the bulldozers.'

This time Vicky didn't return her smile. 'When Alex arrived for lunch—he comes nearly every Sunday, John and the kids like to see him,' she interrupted herself to explain, 'and told me what he'd seen here this morning, he was really bowled over. He said we ought to see it too.' She paused. 'John would've come along, but he's busy pushing through a nasty block round about chapter six. I've lived for years with blocks around chapter six,' she added, on a lighter note, 'so I know the best thing is to leave him to it!'

The warmth in Vicky's tone as she spoke of her husband intrigued Josie. She had little recent experience of family life. 'Where do you live, near here?'

'Right on the edge of Bath—in a small village. Alex lives in the centre, near the office. He has a tiny flat. He's always talking about moving out into the country— but he's so busy designing other people's homes, he never gives himself a chance to think about his own.' They had reached the caravans, and she stopped and turned to Josie. 'How about you—where do you call home, when you're not leading this strange, peripatetic existence?'

Josie hesitated. There was no simple answer to that simple question. 'I live in Cambridge, I suppose. I've been there since I was a student. I work there, but ... I've never really put down roots anywhere. I don't exactly have a home—I share a flat—I've left a few things there, but ...' she shrugged. 'Home is wherever I make it. I'm like a snail—carrying it about with me!' She looked straight at Vicky—defiant, almost, daring her to comment. 'I don't much care where I am. I'm more concerned with what I'm doing at the time.'

But Vicky wasn't one to put her oar in uninvited. 'Alex is just like that,' was all she said. 'You two should get on.'

At that precise moment, as if she had conjured him up, he appeared at the door of the Portacabin. Patiently, gently, he led Matthew down the steep steps; then he turned to make sure the girls were following. The two women watched as the tall figure and the three short ones came towards them—the children running on ahead to greet their mother, the man striding behind.

'Where have you been?' demanded Matthew accusingly. 'I wanted you to see the old things. I saw a

Nancient Roman's penny. And I had a drink of juice.'

'I did see the old things,' his mother reminded him, stooping down to swing him up into her arms. 'I wanted to look at the outside bits again. Thanks, Alex.' She smiled at her old friend and colleague over the top of her son's fair head.

'What for?' He returned the smile; then widened it to include Josie, who was standing in silence, summing him up all over again in the light of everything Vicky had been telling her. 'You know I love these monsters—can't think why.' Emily, who had come to hang on to one of his strong arms, stuck her tongue out at him. 'Anyway, it's all so intriguing, the stuff in there. I could stay here all day, just browsing.'

'You very nearly have,' pointed out Josie, drily.

'That's true.' He faced her squarely now, his gaze direct. 'We mustn't take up any more of your valuable time and space, Miss Barnes. We must be off.'

'Yes, we'd better be getting back,' Vicky agreed. 'John might even be winning his battle with chapter six, and I expect you lot will want your tea.' She smiled, 'It's been great to meet you, Josie. Perhaps we could keep in touch—I could drop by again, if I may?'

'Of course you may. You'd be welcome—any of you,' Josie said carefully.

'Or you might like to come and visit us, at home, if you get fed up with the limitations of caravan life?' Vicky suggested hospitably.

'I'd like that.' Josie accepted the gesture at once—surprising herself. She was usually so reluctant to open up to strangers. But it was hard to think of Vicky in that category, even after such a short acquaintance. Or, for that matter, Alex himself.

He was making purposeful moves to drag them away. 'Now then, Mrs Randle, let's not have one of your prolonged leave-takings. You're all the same, you women, make a three-act drama out of saying a simple goodbye.'

'Don't be a sexist pig,' Rachel reprimanded him sternly. 'We're *not* all the same—are we, Mummy?'

'Absolutely not,' her mother endorsed. 'But I don't think Alex was being entirely serious.'

'You bet I was.' The dark brows met as he brooded at them all to show just how serious he was being. 'So come on, before I come over even more high-handed and order you all to the car.'

'You can't order us about,' chanted Emily. 'You're not our father.'

'Don't be rude, Emily,' Vicky reproached automatically, suppressing a grin. 'Anyway, Daddy doesn't order us about, either.'

But Alex didn't turn a hair. 'In the absence of your father,' he informed Emily, 'I reserve the right to boss you about. So . . .' he rounded on them suddenly, ready to pounce, towering from his full height. '*Off you go!*' Squealing, the children ran off towards the gate. With a smile and a wave to Josie, Vicky followed.

Alex turned back to Josie, smiling again. 'Thank you for giving up so much of your time today. It's been most . . . revealing. I promise not to make a habit of disrupting you—but I'm glad I decided to come by after all.'

Disrupting her! She supposed that was one word for it. Keeping her tone strictly offhand, she replied, 'As I said to Vicky, any of you will be welcome, any time. They're a sweet family,' she added, when he said nothing. 'I like them.'

'That's good. I like my friends to like each other. Goodbye then, Josie. See you sometime.'

'I expect so,' she began, but he was already on his way to join them. Sighing, she set off to chivvy up the last of her team and the few stragglers remaining from the village.

It had been an eventful day, she realised. All at once, she felt flat and exhausted. It was high time she had the place to herself for a while.

CHAPTER THREE

EARLY on Monday morning, Josie set four of her most reliable trainees to work on a new corner of the field. Untouched and thickly grassed over, it lay well beyond the boundary walls of the Roman building itself—but Josie had a private hunch that its innocuous surface concealed something much more interesting. Following up such instincts had always stood her in good stead. As well as sheer know-how, you needed an element of—what was the word Vicky had used about Alex?—flair, that was it, to succeed in this profession just as any other.

By noon they were well under way. After methodically measuring and marking out the area, they started to dig carefully through the top layers of turf and soil, sifting as they went. Josie believed in encouraging their independence, so she left them to it—keeping a weather eye open from not too far away, in case anyone's enthusiasm got the better of his restraint.

At mid-afternoon she had just arrived in the large caravan to snatch a well-earned cup of tea, when a pair of gawky, mud-spattered figures—bright-eyed and breathless—tumbled through the door in hot pursuit. She regarded them patiently while they both poured out their garbled message at once. As soon as she could get a word in edgeways, she suggested: 'Why don't we take it slowly, preferably one at a time?' She turned to the shorter of the two lads. 'Ray—will you try and tell me what's going on?'

The taller youth, who was reasonably conventional in appearance but so bedecked with badges that you could hardly see what he was wearing underneath, draped himself untidily across a small chair, still flushed with eagerness. His companion, close-cropped and stocky, clad in skin-tight jeans, studded leather jacket and Dr Marten boots—took up the tale willingly.

'We did what you told us; started at the edge, worked our way to the middle. We took a quarter each. Tracy had the bit nearest the walls, Dave had the bit next to hers . . .'

'Yes?' Josie prompted. At this rate it could take all day to get to the point. 'And? Have you found something?'

Ray, who never missed a chance of holding the limelight, produced what he hoped was a withering look. 'I was coming to that. We've been digging all day, haven't we, Kev?' His mate nodded emphatically, holding out calloused grubby hands as if to prove it. 'And just now, we found 'em. Kev found the first one, didn't you Kev?'

Fighting a wave of affectionate exasperation, Josie transferred her attention to Kevin, and was met with a triumphant leer. 'The first *what*?' she implored, though she suspected she knew the answer.

She was right. 'Bones!' announced Ray in sepulchral tones. 'Human bones,' he elaborated, enjoying a touch of the macabre. This was the real thing, much better than all those stupid television stories.

But Josie was nodding sagely, disappointingly unimpressed. 'And how do you know they're human?' she enquired mildly.

Ray glared at her reproachfully. He had expected the news to be greeted with—well, if not rapture (which wasn't Josie's style), at least more excitement than this. Still, you never knew with women: they were a law unto themselves. 'You can tell.' His scornful tone indicated his opinion of her question. 'From the sizes and shapes and . . . well, you can just tell. Can't you, Kev?'

The full resources of Kevin's vocabulary swung into action. 'Easy,' he assured Josie 'It's part of a . . .' he considered for a moment. 'Skellington. Just laying there, in the ground.' He marvelled at it all over again.

This time Josie's eyebrows did twitch, her lips did part slightly in controlled anticipation. 'Skeleton?' This was even better than she had hoped. 'Intact? In one piece?'

Ray was mollified. At least this was some kind of reaction, if a low-key one. 'We've only found a few pieces, by they're joined together—aren't they, Kev? You can see it's going to be a person. A small person. Looks like a leg to me—what d'you say, Kev?'

'Yeah, a leg,' Kev confirmed. 'Could be a kid,' he added helpfully.

'Come on then.' Briskly, Josie turned off the gas under the kettle. This was more important than tea. This was what the work was all about. 'Take me to your skeleton. I hope none of you has tried to move it?'

'Of course we ain't,' Ray protested as they ambled after her. 'We just uncovered 'em, like you showed us, and left 'em. What do you think we are, Josie? Stupid?'

She smiled at his pained expression. 'Sorry, Ray— just checking. This might be a major find you've made. Something really important.'

'Okay Josie.' Graciously tolerant, he allowed himself to be placated again.

By Tuesday evening they had unearthed five complete skeletons, as well as some ornaments and utensils which had been buried along with their owners, reinforcing Josie's theory that the graves were pagan. It was arduous, back-bending labour, but their motivation never flagged. Under Josie's calm guidance they worked fast and enthusiastically. She was very pleased with her assistants, and they were even more pleased with themselves.

She saw the four of them off later than usual. 'You've worked really hard these two days,' she congratulated them. 'Don't bust a gut to get here tomorrow. Come whenever you feel like it. I'd like to leave it now, until Simon gets here the day after to have a look.' They all knew her colleague from Cambridge, Simon Raikes, who had been called in before to help with identification and handling of exhibits. 'I don't know about you lot . . .' she yawned and stretched, pushing back her hair, rubbing her eyes, smudging her already dirty cheeks, 'but I'm whacked.'

'Me too.' Tracy jammed a crash helmet on to her sleek head. She always had a lift home on Dave's motorbike.

'And me.' Dave ran a grimy hand through unnaturally yellow hair which stood permanently on end in stiff spikes. 'It was great, though, weren't it?'

'Exciting,' Josie agreed seriously. Secretly thrilling, as she always did to their clear enjoyment, their sheer pleasure in making such vital discoveries. 'So I'll see you when you're ready in the morning, okay? The others will be here at the usual time, but I'll expect you when I see you.'

They hesitated. 'Okay, if you're sure,' Ray said.

She grinned at him and then at Kevin, who was staring doubtfully across at the far corner of the field. 'And don't worry, Kev. I'll guard our babies with my life. They're well covered against marauders—human or animal.'

They straggled off down the track, waving, leaving Josie to her welcome solitude.

She had not been exaggerating when she said she was exhausted. But it was worth every ache, every twinge, she reflected happily as she crossed to the large caravan for a wash before finding herself a bite to eat. Such moments of major revelation in among the hard graft: they were what made the whole process so exhilarating. However many years she went on doing it, she was sure the excitement would never diminish.

She pulled off her boots at the door and padded to the inner cabin. There, she turned the shower taps on and undid half the buttons on her shirt. Then she became aware that the peace of the evening was being shattered by the loud pulse of an engine. Sighing, she did most of the buttons up again, turned off the taps and went to the door to look out. 'No rest for the weary,' she muttered, her eyes on the gate.

Something at the very back of her mind had half-expected it to be the Daihatsu. Perhaps her subconscious memory had recognised its guttural note, the positive sound of its tyres. In any case, she found herself for a second time leaning in a doorway, surveying Alex Grant as he marched purposefully towards her. As before, she displayed no emotion at all: not pleasure, nor displeasure, nor surprise.

With a strong sense of *déjà vu*, she watched as he stopped short at the bottom step. 'We can't go on meeting like this.' The satirical, time-worn cliché hung in the air between them; his deep voice seemed unnervingly familiar. The firm mouth was straight and steady, but a smile flickered in the dark eyes.

'At least it's a different doorway this time.' It sounded silly, but for some reason it was all she could think of to say.

'True; but otherwise I should say we've played this scene before. So what happens next? Do I shake your hand and introduce myself—or could we skip that bit this time?' He was solemn, sardonic.

'I couldn't have come out to meet you—I've got no shoes on.' She sounded sharp, she knew, more defensive than she had intended. They both looked at her feet, which were as small and neat as the rest of her—and encased just now in bright red socks. Suddenly they felt ridiculously bare and exposed; and the sensation spread upwards through her, creating an inexplicable tremor as it went.

'No need to send out a reception committee. I just dropped by on the off-chance of catching you alone—having a quick word.' He was rather tense tonight, she thought, there was a certain tightness behind the confident charm.

'I'm usually alone, after everyone's gone,' she pointed out. 'As a matter of fact, they've only just left. We've been extra-busy since you were last here—it's quite exciting . . .' To her own astonishment, she realised she couldn't wait to tell him the news. 'We've . . .'

'Don't you get lonely when they've gone home?' he interrupted tersely, his eyes fixed on her face. 'Don't you feel a bit isolated? Vulnerable? A woman on her own, stuck out in the middle of nowhere . . .'

'It's hardly that,' she retorted, with some spirit. 'The village is almost within hailing distance and the farm is only just down the track. And I've even got the phone in the Portacabin. Anyway,' she added defiantly, 'I like being alone. I always have.'

'It must be a rough sort of existence, all the same,' he pressed, still eyeing her thoughtfully.

'For a mere female, you mean?' Her eyes flashed scorn at the insulting innuendo.

'I didn't mean that at all. Pin any label on me you like, but I think you'll find, on closer acquaintance, that I'm no male chauvinist—whatever else I may be.' He returned her scowl with a cool gaze that was no less direct.

On closer acquaintance. She hardly knew why, but the words made her stomach clench. She forced an amicable smile. 'I don't go round pinning labels on people, Alex. I'm sorry if I flew off the handle—it always irritates me when anyone suggests women need things cushier than men. You'd be amazed,' she confided, 'at some of the tough situations I've managed, much tougher than this—look at it!' She waved a hand behind her, into the comfortable interior of the large caravan with its two separate compartments, chairs and tables, adequate kitchen facilities, hot and cold running water, flush toilet, electricity—even a small portable television set tucked away in one corner.

He peered at it over her shoulder, raising himself on to tiptoe. 'Hmm—yes. I was forgetting—we'd already laid all the mains services on to this site, hadn't we, before the . . .'

'Before the unexpected delay,' she finished for him. 'Exactly. So, I decided I might as well stay on site and take full advantage of all these mod cons. And even without them,' she assured him, 'I'd have been perfectly okay. The people on the farm are lovely. Mrs Lawson always says I can go round there any time I need anything—even if I fancy a bath. They've been sweet.'

'I thought they sold up when the old man died?' Alex frowned. 'Isn't that why this plot came up for sale in the first place?'

'They only sold a few acres that could be used for building. The rest would never get permission for residential development—strictly agricultural land. You must have known that?' It was her turn to look surprised.

'Yes, I did. But I still thought they'd sold the whole lot and gone.' He looked over to where the farmhouse could just be made out, its old stone walls nestling behind a clump of trees two fields away. Then he lowered his eyes to hers again, smiling. 'I don't care what you say—I'm glad to hear there's someone not too far away to keep an eye on you. I dealt with Mrs Lawson briefly at the time of our initial surveys. She's a nice woman, I remember.'

'Kind of you to be so concerned with my welfare,' Josie remarked drily. It was getting dark, and a chill wind was starting up, cutting across the open plain— and straight through the thin cotton of her shirt. She shivered involuntarily, wrapping her arms protectively around her slight body.

His gaze narrowed on to it, penetrating more effectively than the wind. 'You're not wearing enough, Josie. Shall we go in, or do you want to get a jacket?'

'I was about to have a shower as it happens. I've been trying to say—we've had a particularly hectic day . . .'

'Yes.' Head on one side, he perused the streaks of dirt on her face. 'I do get a sort of impression you've been recently involved in some heavy digging.'

'You can hardly expect to stroll along here of an evening and find me in pristine condition,' she snapped. 'Not a hair out of place, make-up impeccable—like the Hollywood heroines who are still perfect after days of riding through the desert.'

He was totally unabashed. 'God forbid,' he soothed. 'Give me a real woman, not a Hollywood glamour-girl, every time. Anyway, you look absolutely charming with mud on your cheeks. And even better,' he added, catching her flash of irritation, 'when you're cross.' His eyes glinted wickedly into hers.

But Josie refused to rise to that tired old bait. 'If you want to come in and wait while I make myself warm and respectable,' she invited starchily, 'you're welcome. You said you wanted a word. We seem to have had quite a few already—but I really must go in now.' She shivered again, her teeth chattering.

At once he took decisive action—joining her on the top step in one leap, pushing her through the door, closing it firmly behind them—before she could react, let alone complain. Safe inside, he leaned against the closed door, hands in pockets. It was as if he had never moved at all. 'That's better.' He glanced around appreciatively. 'Cosy in here. Now, I'll tell you what.' He seemed to be taking automatic control over the situation. 'Have you eaten yet?' Josie shook her head—wondering why she didn't resent his brisk, organising tone. 'Well,' he instructed, 'get yourself warm—don't bother too much about the "respectable" bit—and I'll take you out to supper. Then you can tell me what you've been up to. We can have . . .' he hesitated for a fraction of a second, 'a proper chat, in more conducive circumstances. How does that sound?'

Conducive to what? she wondered, staring into his face. Her mouth opened and then closed again;

conflicting emotions chased each other across her expression. She was not used to being dominated like this; but Alex did it in such a natural, spontaneous way, it was difficult to summon up the right indignation.

'I don't know . . .' Seeking inspiration, she glanced through the window at the rapidly gathering dusk.

'Go on,' he urged, 'say yes, you know you want to. I bet you don't get out much after work and you look as if you could do with a change of scene.'

'Thanks a million!' But he was right, of course. In the summer, during those endlessly light, balmy evenings, the whole group had often repaired to the garden of the local pub. But when the winter nights drew in, everyone seemed to retire into their shells to hibernate. 'Okay.' He was not the only one capable of reaching a swift decision. 'I'll be ready in ten minutes. Sit down.'

Surprise and pleasure mingled in his smile. 'Great. Never thought I'd persuade you,' he confessed candidly. 'Take your time, there's no hurry. I know how women feel about being rushed.' He stretched himself out, as far as possible, on one of the least spindly chairs, and picked up a newspaper which happened to be lying on the floor.

Refusing to be goaded by his complacent generalisations, Josie tightened her lips and left him to it. First she went back to her own caravan to collect her coat, bag and a suitable change of clothes. When she returned and walked through the outer cabin to the shower cubicle, he appeared to be completely immersed in his newspaper and did not even look up.

Safely the other side of the interconnecting door, she turned on the taps for a second time and started all over again on her shirt buttons. He felt too near for comfort; his presence was a powerful force, reaching to her through the flimsy piece of plywood which separated them. But she peeled off all her clothes, tucked her fine mane into a bathcap, stepped under the steaming spray and drew the plastic curtain round her.

Such modest scruples were just so much nonsense, she lectured herself turning up her face, revelling in the soft warmth of the water, richly lathering scented soap on to her pale smooth skin. Maidenly inhibitions were hardly her style. She was no stranger to men as ... fairly intimate companions, after all. The occasional ship that passed in the night; once in a while, a brief encounter to ease the tension of her body and the loneliness of her soul. As long as she felt protected from any risk of true involvement—as long as her head ruled her heart with a rod of steel—she allowed these things to happen, just now and then.

She turned off the taps and groped for her huge towel, enveloping her small frame with it. The problem was, of course, that none of that had ever really worked. The tension of her body might be eased, for a short while. It could even be fun. But the emptiness in her soul—that was another matter. If anything, such meaningless, peripheral contact only deepened it.

She had friends who were men, just as she had friends who were women—though not very many of either. Over the years, a few of them had expressed a different kind of attraction, had made attempts to intensify the relationship into something much deeper; but Josie fought shy of any such suggestion. As far as she was concerned friends were friends, and lovers were lovers. They belonged in two separate, distinct categories; and the firm line between them must never be permitted to blur. If it did, she suspected, that would be inviting disaster. The precise nature of the disaster was not quite clear to her—only that it was inevitable unless you avoided anything resembling a commitment.

Work: that was the great safety net. As long as she had that cocoon to wind round herself she knew she was secure. What did she need from other people? Socially, as long as she had her independence, she got on fine. Sexually, she had discovered quite early on, there was always some like-minded man, ready and waiting to fulfil her needs. Men had been using women that way for centuries, after all, hadn't they? Why shouldn't it be only natural for both sexes?

It was all so simple really; she never understood what people made so much fuss about. Love? Surely you could escape that useless, indefinable emotion—as long as you kept to the hard-and-fast rule: never overturn that invisible but vital barrier between friendship and desire.

She brushed out her soft curls vigorously, and dressed quickly in a neat brown flared skirt and a clean cream blouse with a pretty striped sleeveless pullover. It felt peculiar, pulling on a brand-new pair of tights, fitting her feet into her one pair of smart shoes. How long had it been since she had worn anything other than old jeans and boots or lace-up sneakers? Weeks, she suspected. Probably not since Christmas, which she had spent with friends in Cambridge; a family who had made her very welcome as always—but with whom, as always, she had felt something of an intruder, an outsider. She sighed: Josie Barnes, one of life's perpetual outsiders. Was that how it had to be?

Exactly ten minutes after leaving him, she presented herself to Alex, who was now contentedly chewing his pen as he filled in the crossword. He looked up; and the heavy brows lifted, widening the expressive dark eyes as they carried out a full and detailed inspection. 'Wow! What a speedy transformation—and an effective one. I'm honoured, Miss Barnes; it will be a privilege to escort you.' He stood up, glancing down at his own casual cords and plaid shirt. 'I only hope I don't let the side down,' he remarked with a gleam.

'Don't be stupid.' More than a little ungraciously, she threw the compliment back in his face. 'You look fine, and you know it.' Whatever he wore, her mind pointed out irritatingly, Alex Grant would look fine. He was a very goodlooking man—and a powerfully attractive one at that. What a pity, it nagged, he was really rather a nice one as well. What the hell was she doing, then, going out with a lethal combination like that?

If he wondered why she was lowering at him like a small thundercloud, he made no sign. He simply grinned and picked up his jacket. 'Let's hit the road then. I'm starving. What do you feel like eating?'

He strode ahead of her to hold the door open so that she could go through first. It was a naturally chivalrous gesture, she told herself reasonably, trying not to let her body stiffen as it brushed gently against his in the narrow entrance. 'Anything not too fancy, I'm easy.' Sorting through a bunch of keys, she locked up both caravans and the Portacabin. 'What did you have in mind?'

'Well, we could go to Bath. Or there's a little place I know not all that far away—in a village—where they do really good simple food. Shouldn't be booked up on a weekday, with any luck.' Spontaneously helpful, he supported her elbow as they crossed the uneven grass.

'Sounds just the sort of thing I like.' As soon as they reached the gate, she withdrew her arm. Fumbling with the overloaded keyring, she found the biggest one and turned it in the mortice lock. Then she snapped the heavy padlock into place on its chain. 'Can't be too careful,' she muttered, conscious of his wry grin as he watched her.

'Got to batten down the hatches,' he agreed. 'You have a heavy responsibility, haven't you Josie?' he added more seriously.

'Don't want anyone breaking in and messing things up—or stealing things,' she told him grimly. 'Even a careless foot treading in the wrong place can set us back weeks. And we can't spare weeks, even though we're doing quite well.'

He helped her up into the passenger seat of the jeep before coming round to his own side. 'Time-wise, you mean?' He clicked his seat-belt together, then reached over, nonchalantly, to fasten hers. She opened her mouth to tell him she could manage it perfectly well—and then thought better of it. There was nothing calculated about his actions—he was a straightforward man: surely that was obvious? No point in being unnecessarily argumentative.

'Not too badly, time-wise,' she said. 'Or otherwise.'

'You mean you're ahead of your schedule?' He sounded so hopeful, eager, that she flicked a curious glance at him. His profile, in the dimness, was vague and yet oddly defined; the neat beard giving it a fine, almost classical appearance—like the head of an emperor on an ancient coin.

'We're never ahead of schedule,' she replied as he started the engine. 'We always need more time than we've got. But I think we should make it in time, with this project. After all, there's still a year to go.'

He said nothing, concentrating on the dark road as they bowled away from the village. The countryside stretched out to both sides—alien and mysterious under a half-moon and the first hesitant stars. Josie stared through her window at it, enjoying a strange sense of release—and the bouncing ride in the ruggedly unfamiliar vehicle.

They maintained a companionable silence until they were established at a small corner table in the cosy country restaurant. When they had ordered, Alex leaned back in his chair, hands linked behind his glossy dark head, smiling at her—relaxed, encouraging. 'So—what's with this piece of excitement you've been dying to regale me with ever since I arrived?'

Startled, she caught his eye. Surely it had not been that obvious? She liked to think she was more subtle, more controlled than that. Then she shrugged and returned his smile. 'Oh, just a few bodies we've dug up,' she told him airily.

'Bodies?' He frowned, sceptical now. 'Corpses, you mean? An unsolved crime? Ghastly secrets on the fringes of Summerford?'

'Not that kind of bodies. Roman, or even pre-Roman, remains. *Skellingtons,* as one of my trainees called them.'

His eyebrows lifted. 'Graves?'

'That's right. A whole row of pagan graves—complete with artifacts.'

'That sounds important. Did you expect it?' He was studying her closely.

'It's important—no doubt about that. I half-expected it, yes—they had to dispose of their dead somewhere, and it wasn't hygienic within the precincts, so they often put them just outside—but not too far away.' She grew more animated and lit up as she recalled the excitement of the discovery. 'You should have seen their faces, when they found the first bones, four of my team that is. You'd have thought they were personally responsible for the whole thing. Since then they've worked really hard—and so have I.' She rubbed ruefully at one stiff shoulder.

'How many do you think there are?' There was fascination in his eyes—but caution too somewhere behind it: this strange reserve.

'Well, we've unearthed five complete ones so far. Could be several more—maybe even lots. These are all in a neat line orientated north-south. There may be some Christian ones as well, facing east-west, somewhere near. I've got a colleague coming over Thursday to see what he thinks, he's more of an expert on this than I am.'

'Will it take a long time?' Alex was openly—almost sharply—curious now.

'Well, it never does to rush these things. My personal opinion is that it could take weeks before we've found what there is, and after that we have to organise a careful analysis of our findings. It's not the sort of job that can be done overnight,' she reminded him briskly. Then she flashed a grin at him. 'So far, we haven't found any men. Two of them are children, and I'm pretty sure the others are women. There may well be a whole separate graveyard for the men. Inequality of the sexes, even in death,' she remarked.

He grinned back, but half-heartedly seeming somehow detached. 'Well done. That's most impressive, Josie. You must be delighted—no wonder you were all glowing when I arrived today.'

She looked down at her hands, embarrassed. 'Muddy, more like,' she muttered.

'That too. It was a heart-warming spectacle.' His voice was warm and suggestive.

She was saved from further confusion by the arrival of their first course; and after a few mouthfuls she realised how hungry she was. They had both chosen the home-made hotpot which headed the brief menu chalked up on a blackboard on the wall, and it proved to be delicately savoury and aromatic. With it they shared a bottle of red wine, a salad and a generous basket of french bread.

Suitably relaxed, she was on the point of demanding an explanation for his visit, when he changed tack completely, steering the conversation on to a more personal level. 'Where do you come from, Josie? Any family?'

She put down her fork, taken aback by the question. 'I was born in London. I left when I went to Cambridge. I don't like big cities. And no, I haven't got any family,' she enlightened him bluntly.

He paused, a forkful of food halfway to his mouth. 'None at all? No parents, grandparents—no one?'

'My grandparents have been dead for years. My mother . . . died when I was in my teens. I lost touch with my father about then—he might as well be dead—probably is, for all I know.' *Or care*, her tone implied. 'I've got no sisters or brothers—there was just me.' An edge of fierce bitterness cut through her tone, for all her attempts to keep it cool. She swallowed.

'How about you?' She managed a weak smile. 'I'd guess you're part of a big family?'

He had been listening to her intently, watching her closely, now he laughed, breaking the unexplained tension which flowed from her. 'Right first time. One of six, no less—I come in the middle. Three sisters, two brothers. Born and bred in Edinburgh,' he informed her proudly, 'but came south to college—and stayed here ever since, though I sometimes wonder why! The rest of the clan are all still up there, including my parents, still going strong.'

Now he mentioned it, she had noticed the trace of a lilt to his voice—just a hint, nothing broad, a softening here and there, a rounding of the 'o' in the way he said her name . . . 'Do you miss them?' What would it be like, she wondered wistfully—being part of a real family like that?

'I did at first; but you have to make your own life. And Bath's a fine old city—almost as fine as Edinburgh. I visit them when I can. I've got so many nephews and nieces up there, I've lost count.' He refilled both their glasses with careful concentration, his hand steady on the bottle. Quietly he went on: 'I'm sorry about your parents. It sounds . . . sad. Do you want to tell me about it?'

'No.' The bleak monosyllable echoed between them. Realising he had meant the suggestion kindly, she added hastily, 'Thanks. It's okay, I'm used to it, I just don't think about it any more.'

Exactly what she just didn't think about was obscure; but he let it drop as their desserts arrived. For the next hour or so, as they lingered over delicious gateaux from the trolley, excellent black coffee, even—for a change— a small cognac, Josie found herself unwinding and expanding in his lively company. It amazed her, and yet it seemed so natural, the way they conversed easily about such a wide variety of objective topics. She was not used to establishing such a rapport with anyone— least of all any man—after so short a time. They agreed and sympathised often enough to make it satisfying; and they disagreed and argued often enough to make it stimulating. And whenever the conversation threatened even to touch on anything dangerously personal, Alex had skilfully—almost imperceptibly—manoeuvred it into calmer, safer waters before Josie could react and clam up.

Whether it was excitement at this degree of sensitivity on his part, or simply the result of several glasses of smooth red wine followed by the brandy, she found herself feeling uncharacteristically light-headed, and even giggly. 'I don't usually get much chance to indulge in creature comforts during a dig,' she confided, nursing the balloon-shaped glass. 'Mustn't get too soft—it might put me off my concentration tomorrow. Can't have my team think I'm slipping.'

'You deserve a break. Enjoy it while you've got the chance.' There was that slight note of enigma under his simple words again, as if they might suggest more. But she was far too relaxed and contented to follow the thought up. 'You know what they say: all work, no play?'

'From what I heard, you could do with taking your own advice,' she commented.

'I suppose my esteemed partner's been gossiping about me behind my back?' His brows beetled in mock indignation. 'Always on at me, that one. A mother, through and through. Leaves her own brood at home and then comes and fusses over me.'

'*Married to the job* was the phrase she used, I believe.' Josie gazed into the amber depths of her brandy glass.

'Then I suspect that's something else you and I have in common, Josie.' The deep brown eyes, levelled on to hers, drove the point home accurately as usual. She did not deny it: there seemed no need.

It was midnight when they drew up outside the fence. The site was shrouded in velvet black. The gate was barely visible, and the vans no more than ghostly shapes. Josie cursed herself for a fool: in her haste to get ready to leave, she had forgotten that most basic necessity of night life in an area like this—a torch!

Switching off the ignition, he turned to face her—reduced to a gleam of eyes, a flash of teeth and suddenly very close in the thick darkness. Suddenly an indefinable threat rather than a comfortable companion.

She cleared her throat. 'Well, thanks Alex. I must be going in—it's late.'

'You'll be needing this then.' With a flourish he produced a large tough flash-lamp from under the dashboard and pressed its button, flooding them both with its powerful beam; casting angular shadows across his deeply-etched features. She was immediately torn between resentment and gratitude at his efficiency. One hand pointing the torch, the other firmly guiding her, he saw her safely to her caravan.

Standing on the lowest step, she faced him. 'I won't ask you in if you don't mind, Alex. I've got a busy day tomorrow, and I'm sure you have too, and it's very late, and I'm really rather tired, and . . .'

'Josie,' he cut in softly. 'I wasn't going to come in anyway. It's all right.' He switched off the torch. The night was a black cloak descending, clinging all round them.

She struggled against a crazy sensation of disappointment at his words. He was being entirely sensible, and she should be relieved that he shared her own attitude. 'Right. Well, that's okay then. As long as we understand each other,' she said stiffly. 'I'll see you sometime. Thanks again.' Turning, she began to climb the rest of the steps.

But his hands caught her from behind, swivelling her round to face him again. 'Just because I'm not coming in,' he murmured, very low, 'doesn't mean I wouldn't appreciate a simple salutation. You're lovely, Josie Barnes—and you have a lovely mouth. I've been looking at it all evening.' At every word he drew her closer, until his warm breath played on her cheeks and chin. His lips against hers whispered: 'I've been thinking about it ever since I set eyes on it.'

She put up no fight. Surely it could do no harm, that time-honoured institution—a goodnight kiss, stolen on the doorstep? The most inexperienced adolescent might expect no less. A harmless tradition—sweet, innocent, superficial. The least she could offer after such a pleasant evening. She surrendered her lips to his willingly, without reluctance; letting him taste them, brush his over them, infinitely soft and gentle.

It was sweet—very sweet; and she relaxed against him. Then, abruptly, there was nothing innocent about it, or superficial. Before she could even register the change his demands had deepened, and she had opened to him; and his tender, tentative explorings had exploded into a mutual fire. There was nothing adolescent about the cravings which leaped instantly to life in her—convulsive responses, flowing down her veins like quicksilver, shooting flames through her body. All at once, whatever had sprung up between Alex and herself was entirely, unarguably, adult. And not safe—not safe at all.

She pulled away, gasping, heaving with all her strength against his chest—desperate to put distance between them, as far and as fast as possible. But he held her firmly by the upper arms, hard fingers gripping, hurting—staring at her through inches of thick darkness. His voice rasped sounding hoarse, unfamiliar, but controlled. 'What is it, Josie? What's the matter?'

'Nothing. I . . .' She twisted this way and that, agonised, almost in tears.

'Hey, hey.' He was calmer now; his grip loosened. Free to escape, she just stood there her arms hanging limp at her sides, her gaze lowered. 'It was meant to be a friendly gesture—nothing more. Nothing alarming.' He peered closely into her face, and she flinched from the shrewdness in his eyes—a tangible quality. 'I don't believe you're that green and untouched, Josie, any more than I am, and I'm not,' he assured her tersely. 'I think you wanted that to happen, as much as I did. So—why not?'

She shook her head, hating herself for being so helpless, so lost for words. This was not the real her, she wanted to tell him. Something peculiar had happened to her poise. She didn't usually ... 'Alex, I didn't ... I don't really ...'

'Don't say you don't like me.' He chuckled, his equanimity returning. 'I won't believe you. I haven't given you any reason not to like me—yet.' His tone darkened again. 'I was under the impression we were getting on all right.'

'It's not that, Alex.' She was recovering her dignity at last. 'It's not that I don't like you.' *Far from it*, her mind screamed: she liked him a lot—far too much to risk this sort of contact. It was against everything she believed in—a chance she never let herself take. 'I just don't feel like it tonight, that's all,' she lied lamely. 'If you don't mind.' That was the liberated, the civilised excuse, she taunted herself wrily. *Not feeling like it tonight*. No man but a bully had an answer to that, surely?

But he cupped her face gently between his hands. 'Of course I mind, Josie. I'm only flesh and blood—and you're an extremely attractive woman—as I'm quite sure you're well aware. But I've already told you, I had no intention of ...' he hesitated, 'trespassing on your hospitality tonight anyway ... whether you'd invited me in—or not. It's not my habit to take advantage of any woman on such slight acquaintance, however tempting she may be.' He shrugged, letting her go; she was sure, in the darkness, that he was half-smiling. 'I'll accept your decision—take it like a man ... for the moment. But,' he promised, his tone very low, 'I'll be back. Very soon. We,' he assured her, 'have barely begun.'

There was something, mingled threat and insinuation in his voice, which caused the hairs to rise at the back of her neck. But she kept her voice steady, schooling herself firmly to her mature self again. 'Goodnight then, Alex.' Reaching up, she planted a quick light kiss on his bearded cheek—the most she should have allowed in the first place. Then she turned and walked up the steps and through the door, not looking back once.

He waited until she was safely inside, without another word; then he swung round on his heel and strode briskly away, the searching ray of his flashlight streaming ahead of him.

Secure in her haven, drawing her dainty curtains, lighting the lamp, Josie watched the jeep's tail lights disappear towards the main road. As she got ready for bed, it occurred yet again to her weary mind that she still hadn't dug out the real reason for his unexpected, unexplained appearance there tonight. However personal his interest claimed to be, she could swear there was something more to it than that. *I'll be back*: with a slight *frisson* she recalled the simple words and the tone they'd been spoken in. She had known him all of three days; but a strong instinct told her he was a man who kept to his expressed intentions. He would be back.

For a few minutes she lay, her head filled with burning questions, her body with burning recollections. Then sheer exhaustion pushed her over the edge, and she was asleep.

CHAPTER FOUR

EIGHT hours later, the letter arrived.

By nine o'clock, Josie had been up and ready for half an hour. Even though she had told her four stalwarts to take some of the morning off the rest would duly arrive at their usual time; and she always made a point of being prepared for them. It was her nature to avoid being caught out by anyone—or anything.

The postman's red van screeched to a halt, as it usually did, in the mud outside the gate. Josie walked over to take the letters from him, exchanging a few cheery words about the fine morning. Then she watched as the van continued on down the track to the farm.

Turning to go back to the caravan, she sorted through what looked like a routine batch of correspondence. Two from Cambridge: one would be a report on some small items she had sent over for analysis, the other was from one of her flatmates. Then there was the predictable dull manila, doubtless containing bills ... and what was this? Neatly typed, postmarked Bristol—a long, official-looking white envelope. Reaching the caravan, she tore it open first.

She sank into a chair at the tiny table and sat for several minutes, staring at the letter. The more she read, the less sense the words seemed to make. Her head swam as she forced herself to put its message together— to take it calmly—not to react till she was sure she had got it right.

It was headed *Wallace Holdings*. Well, she'd had those before. Nothing alarming about that. *Dear Miss Barnes*, it began, harmlessly enough. *We regret to have to inform you that a decision was reached at the last meeting of our Board of Directors ... due to a change of*

policy at Board level ... the period of time initially
allocated to your Project will now have to be curtailed ...
the Building Contractors wish to resume operations
within three months ...

Less than three months? They couldn't do it to her!
It wasn't possible—it was unheard-of for a company
to back out of its commitment so suddenly, without
warning. It just was not done. Decent people didn't
behave in this high-handed manner. They had set a
definite time-limit; they couldn't simply override it at
the drop of a Director's whim ... ruin all her
meticulous planning ... spoil every chance of completing the excavations that were going so successfully.

Blood boiling, eyes flashing, she marched to the
Portacabin and picked up the telephone. There was
no way—*no way!*—she was going to sit by and let
these faceless bureaucrats stamp out her precious dig.
Clutching the fateful piece of paper, she dialled the
number at the top of it and ordered the switchboard
operator to connect her to the right extension. Then
she waited, drumming her fingers impatiently, sum-
moning up every ounce of righteous indignation at
her disposal.

The Managing Director himself was not, of course,
available. Probably never appeared in the office before
lunch, she thought scathingly—pushing her way
verbally past a bored, nasal secretary to the most
exalted minion she was able to conjure up. His
perfectly-oiled tones flowed down the receiver at her—
meeting her rage with a much deadlier weapon:
placatory complacency.

'Naturally, we realise you are bound to feel upset,
Miss Barnes.'

'Upset!' she spluttered, waving the letter at the
telephone as if to shove it under his unctuous nose. 'I
should think I am upset! Don't you see what this
means? Our timing was already tight to the last week.
We can't possibly manage to finish what we've already

started within three months—let alone start on anything new.'

'The Board has attempted to convey to you, in its letter, how deeply it regrets the decision,' he assured her, as smooth as cream. 'Unfortunately, circumstances beyond our control . . .'

'What do you mean?' she interrupted bluntly. 'Beyond your control? Beyond *whose* control?'

'Beyond the immediate control of the Board,' he explained glibly. 'The Contractors have put their foot down . . . rising prices . . . financial considerations . . .'

His words merged together, a meaningless jumble of platitudes. 'Doesn't The Board consist of human beings?' she demanded heatedly. 'Isn't there a beating heart anywhere in that—that impersonal machine? Can't you *understand* what it's going to mean—not only to me—to the local people? And to a whole group of young workers who are just getting to the most rewarding part of the dig? And to the Archaeological profession as a whole? Don't you have any feeling for the wider . . .'

'We do appreciate how difficult this makes matters for you, Miss Barnes.' His show of spurious sympathy was totally unconvincing. 'That's why we have gone out of our way to give you as much notice as we could.'

'Three months! Big deal!' Her fury only grew in direct proportion to his silky politeness. 'How much do you expect us to achieve in that time? It's *nine* months less than the absolute minimum I originally specified—and you accepted,' she reminded him pointedly. 'I'm not superhuman. In three months there's no way I can get round to the rest of what this site has to offer. It'll be broken up—buried desecrated.' Her voice rose to a dramatic pitch. 'Just for the sake of some—some petty bureaucratic decision!' She spat the last three words out as if they were poison.

He remained unmoved—only, perhaps, a little wounded. 'I'm sorry you feel like that,' he declared, never raising his own voice above its bland monotone. 'The Board hoped you would accept its reasoning, see its difficulties . . .'

'Damn the Board!' She could almost see him cringe as she took the name of this sanctified body in vain. 'You can tell the Board from me that it can take its . . .' she glanced at the first paragraph of the letter, '. . . *change in policy*, and . . .'

He cut in hastily before she could go into lurid detail. 'We did hope,' he pointed out, 'that if you were to attend the Special Meeting, you might have the opportunity to hear more about this policy decision— put your own case,' he invited graciously—making it quite clear, all the same, that whatever she said would make no difference at all to an already sewn-up conclusion.

'What Special Meeting?' she growled, suspicious.

'I believe you will find a reference to it in the final section of your letter,' he informed her with exaggerated patience.

Feeling slightly sheepish, she looked at the letter again. In her shocked dismay she had hardly taken in the last few sentences. He was quite correct: she was cordially invited to attend a meeting on Friday afternoon at which the matter would be fully discussed by all parties concerned.

'But that's the day after tomorrow!'

'Indeed it is,' he conceded kindly. 'Are we to take it, then, that you intend to be present?'

'I certainly do,' she retorted grimly: 'And you can tell the Board that I'll have a thing or two to say. They needn't think they can get away with this—not while they've got me to contend with. I've got contacts,' she told him darkly. 'The Project's sponsors—and the County Council. What are *they* going to say about all this?'

'I think you'll find,' he replied, oozing smugness, 'that the funding agencies have already been informed of the decision, and have given their—albeit reluctant—support to the curtailing of the scheme.' *Well, they would*, Josie's mind droned. *Less money for them to find*. 'The Local Authority is—somewhat less convinced,' he went on carefully, 'but we have every confidence that we can bring them round to our point of view.'

'Bully them into submission, you mean,' remarked Josie rudely. 'I suppose they'll all be at this meeting, too?'

'We expect full representation of all parties involved,' he agreed.

An appalling thought chilled her to the bone, 'Including the Architects of the development?'

'I imagine so,' he confirmed—allowing himself the barest touch of surprise.

'Did they—know about this?' She forced her tone to a lower, more detached level.

'I should imagine so,' he repeated—beginning to sound bored by this conversation. Doubtless he had far more important things to do than chat to irate female archaeologists—despite the need for effective public relations which were his forté as front-man for his company. 'You will be able to ascertain that. Now, if I can't help you any further, Miss Barnes, I am wanted on my other line . . .'

In a flash, she pictured him: a suave, dapper man in an immaculate striped business suit; relaxed in his plush, orderly office; surrounded by smart, efficient secretaries. On his vast new desk would be one or two pompous-looking files and documents—not too many—as well as at least three push-button telephones, of different colours.

'I won't keep you, then,' she said coldly. 'But make sure you register my total opposition to this policy decision at the highest level.'

'I shall do so, Miss Barnes.' His good breeding never slipped by a millimetre. 'Thank you so much for ringing. Goodbye.'

And thank you for nothing, her mind screamed as she slammed down the receiver without deigning to reply. Then she sat for a full minute, glaring at the phone itself as if he was compressed inside it—he, and all he stood for.

She glanced out of the window: the first of her team were arriving now: on bikes and motorbikes, or on foot from the bus stop near the village. She must brace herself to appear normal—cheerful and brisk. No point in letting them suffer—not yet; not until it was irrevocable. Once again she seethed, just contemplating the arrogance, the sheer cruelty of it. So much history, so much knowledge of humanity to be uncovered—and so many peoples' lives involved—and they thought they could ride roughshod over the whole Project as if it was no more than a trivial game!

She wondered fleetingly whether there might be a legal loophole she could climb through in order to escape their vast, impersonal machinery. But no—a company like this would surely have done their homework before backing out of such a commitment, even if it was informally made. She would have to fight the thing on some other basis. But what weapon did she—or the combined interests of her profession—hold against such a monstrous enemy?

After all, she reflected, staring through the window—look what they've done to our poor world. In the war of past versus present, there was little doubt who was winning. Nothing around us would ever be the same again; and if powerful giants like Wallace Holdings had their way, we wouldn't even get the chance to discover the tiniest clues left us by our own heritage. It was so sad, it made her—literally—sick. She could feel the taste of it, strong and acrid at the back of her throat.

She set off as efficiently as possible about her business for the day, greeting her team, getting them going on their usual tasks. As far as she could, she concentrated on the work in hand, shelving the pressing problem until she had time to herself to think it over. But, as the hours wore on, there was no disguising the extra dimension which insidiously added itself to her sense of disgust and betrayal. It was not just the massive firm and all they stood for. It was not just the battle of past and present. It was not even the strong-arm tactics of a world of insensitive men. It was—of course it was—the part played in all this by Alexander Grant.

When she forced herself to face it, she knew just how blindly stupid she had been. She could have kicked herself; and if he had been there, she would quite probably have kicked him. He had known about this all along—that was obvious—from the first moment he had set foot here at the site. The messages were there, glaring, if she had only cared to pick them up. He had arrived there, nosing out the imminent possibilities, plotting the next stages, revising his earlier plans—relishing the prospect of getting his show on the road again sooner than expected. He had blatantly employed all that macho charm, that outward involvement and sensitivity, to get beneath her defences—soften her up for the inevitable process just ahead. No doubt, she reflected bitterly, he had been set up to it by the great moguls of Wallace Holdings themselves—who knew his skills at human manipulation as well as they respected his architectural ones.

She was so incensed, so shocked, that she had to stop in her tracks and take a few deep breaths to steady herself. Fancy letting herself come half under the spell of a hypocrite like that! With all her hard-headed experience, fancy allowing things to come to that stage—and in only three days! It was shameful, disgusting. It did not bear thinking about. She was sickened—with herself as much as with Alex Grant.

And then, bringing Vicky along—another woman, no less, and she had seemed so nice ... how they must have laughed at her once they had got away; showing them round, proudly describing her finds—when all the time, they had only wanted to renew their acquaintance with their site—*their* site, not hers! How they must have gloated over her naïve acceptance of their professed interest in her activities there!

And as if that was not enough, he had come back for more last night—treating himself to an extra laugh, no doubt, at her expense. Those quizzical, enigmatic glances—that unspoken, underlying tension he had emanated—some of his remarks, or near-remarks: suddenly they all fell into place, pieces in a jigsaw. For the tenth time, she gritted her teeth, cursing her own lack of caution. For the first time in her life, she had let a man through the outer layers of her armour; and it had to be the time that really mattered. What tales had he taken back to his colleagues, she wondered, about her ingenuousness? Well, at least she hadn't added the label 'pushover' to her other mortifications! Doubtless that was what he had been hoping to achieve, turning up like that last night, but he had been thwarted. He would never know it, of course; but the true irony was that if she had not liked him so much—found him so compatible, so stimulating as a person and as a man— she would never have hesitated to comply with his plans on that front, either.

Well, he was never going to know that, or anything else about her. From this moment, she had nothing more to do with him. She would fight her way through the mess as best she could; and Simon would arrive next day to add moral support, at least that was something. He was probably the only man in the world she could trust. His interests in this affair would be her interests: she could be sure of that, if of nothing else. She lifted her chin defiantly; set her face into a composed mask. No one else was going to guess that anything was wrong. And she would put her crazy reaction to Alex Grant down to bitter experience—a useful object lesson that even she was not totally impervious, after all. If he

chose to loom on the fringes of her life again, she would
send him packing; or, more maturely, treat him with the
cold contempt he merited.

She was to have an opportunity to put this resolution
to the test a good deal sooner than she had expected. At
seven o'clock in the evening—less than an hour after
she had seen the last of her workers off, just as she was
preparing her usual snack meal—the Daihatsu was at
the gate again. She knew its unmistakable sound by
now: it had become ingrained deep in her mind already,
setting off signals, triggering off responses which had
nothing to do with her conscious self.

She stiffened all over, sneaking a confirming glance
out of the window as the now-familiar figure made his
positive way in her direction. Then she sighed and
slumped into a chair, burying her weary face in her
hands as she summoned up the degree of strength of
character this new challenge was going to demand.
Determination and steely resolve were all very well, in
theory. Being called upon to put them into almost
instant practice, when you were tired and drained and
anxious, was something else again.

But her anger soon came to her rescue, reliable as
ever. It did not take much effort to remember just what
this man had done to her, how shabbily he had treated
her. Refusing even to explain the object of his visits—
when it must be patently clear to him that she had no
idea, as yet, what was going on! Not bothering to warn
her ... on the contrary, breaking down her natural
defences so that she was quite unprepared when the
blow did come ... How dare he show his face here now,
tonight? How dare he come swanning into her field,
confident and poised as if nothing had happened?

She was ready for him when he arrived, opening her
caravan door just as he was on the point of knocking,
taking him by surprise as he stood on the threshold,
knuckles raised in mid-air. Standing on the second step,
his eyes were level with hers; and she took full

advantage of the opportunity this gave her to stare straight into them.

'Good-evening, Alex.' The greeting was ice-cold and hostile: no greeting at all.

'Hallo, Josie.' He didn't flinch; he didn't even have the grace to look abashed.

'You seem to be having some difficulty in keeping away from here,' she pointed out with heavy sarcasm. 'To what do I owe the honour this time? Come to complete your . . . investigations? Or perhaps to crow over your petty victory?' A faint frown had gathered his dark brows together, and a succession of fleeting reactions was crossing his expression—puzzlement, irritation, irony—even, for a moment, sympathy. She continued in the same stridently caustic tone before he could comment. 'You've missed your vocation, Mr Grant. You should have gone on the stage. Your performance these last few days has been positively oscar-worthy. I never guessed a thing. There I was, allowing myself to think your interest in this site was at least partly altruistic . . . even,' she added, unable to hone down the bitterness that edged her words, 'personal. And all the time you were just keeping the wheels of industry oiled, ready to run over our little achievements here.'

Far from disconcerted, he was regarding her with deep, direct curiosity—laced with a clear hint of wry concern. For several moments, at the end of this long speech, he remained absolutely silent. Then he shook his head slightly, his eyes still on hers. 'So.' It was more of a statement than a question. 'You've finally heard.'

There seemed no point in denying it. 'I had the letter this morning.' She shrugged, almost nonchalantly, as if she was used to the idea already. If acting was the order of the day, two could play at that game. 'I'd have thought,' she observed acidly, 'even you might be too much of a gentleman to come trampling on a woman when she's well and truly down.'

If she was keeping her sharp pain and resentment on a tight leash, he was no less constrained—deliberately patient, impassive. 'I was . . .' he began softly.

'*Just passing?*' she mocked, almost allowing the control to slip. '*Thought you'd look in on the off-chance? Wanted to have a word?* We've been through all that, Alex!' There was scorn in every line of her taut body. 'Get to the point—if there is one.' A touch of shrillness was creeping into her voice now, despite all her efforts to stay cool. 'As far as I'm concerned, there's no more to be said. Perhaps we had—we might have had—something to . . . say to each other; but not now.'

'Josie.' The single sound, her name, compelled her attention—something in the way he said it bringing her up short, cutting off her rising anger. She did not understand why, but she knew she had to listen to him. 'I was worried about you.' The five simple words, spoken with slow deliberation, defied her to interrupt or contradict. 'And I disagree with you. We *have* got to talk. There *is* more to say. Aren't you going to ask me in? I won't keep you long.'

She ignored his last suggestion. 'Worried about me? You were *worried* about me? That's a good one!' She managed an extremely dry laugh. 'You mean you haven't come looking for the last ounce of your pound of flesh?'

Even as she used the phrase, she knew all at once how she should be playing this tricky scene. *Your pound of flesh* . . . of course, that was it. Flesh. Now that the truth was out, the man and his real motives exposed, she could afford to allow her natural instincts to take over. She certainly did not like him, not now: in fact she hated him. She was safe from emotional risk after all—back in her snug, armour plated cocoon. She could fight like with like. She could give as good as she had got. She could make use of him, even welcome his attentions, indulge her own needs—and then spit him out afterwards, as he had planned to do: rejected, no longer necessary. The ultimate weapon—used down the ages, from mythology onwards, by both sexes in the war against each other. Perhaps she had never quite reached this level of blatant, dispassionate objectivity— but it was not so very alien to her nature after all. She was on safe, familiar territory. She could invite him into her web, like the lethal female spider; and afterwards, however *he* might feel, *she'd* be intact, unscathed— victorious.

With that decided, she felt more confident. Before he could reply to her taunt, she went coolly on. 'Well, since you're showing such involvement in my affairs, perhaps you had better come in.' She stood aside to let him pass, deliberately narrowing the space so that he was forced to slide against her in the process. She hardened herself to ignore the very real sensations this brief contact aroused in her. Damn the man! She was nowhere near immune to him yet! But she had embarked on this plan of action now; and she was going through with it.

He sat down on the bunk; but she remained standing, keeping her advantage where she could find it. Leaning against the closed door, she stared into his eyes with what she hoped was provocative challenge. He returned the gaze with his usual—yet so unusual—combination of warmth and hooded irony.

'You really didn't know a thing about it, then?'

'You know very well I didn't,' she confirmed levelly. 'Otherwise you wouldn't have . . .' she bit back the beginnings of a revealingly furious retort. She must not give way to that—not even for a moment. 'Whereas you, on the other hand,' she accused cynically, 'have been fully aware of the situation all along? How kind it might have been,' she jeered unpleasantly, 'if you'd seen fit to share the vital information with me!'

'I knew.' It was a straightforward acknowledgement, without shame. 'But we were told in confidence. Some time ago, in fact. I did think, when I came here, that you'd know as well . . .'

'Oh, not me!' she scoffed—her tone clearly indicating she did not believe a syllable of it. 'All the important people get put in the picture soon enough; you lot—financiers, developers, builders, planners . . . architects. The big boys. Never mind us—the harmless, well-meaning little diggers up of dreams. We'll get told when you're good and ready. When we've been suitably sussed out, and buttered up, and—and infiltrated . . .' She swallowed hard and then sucked in a long breath. She was letting out too much. This was not the way she had decided on.

He countered pained sarcasm with light irony. 'Oh yes, we all knew ages ago. Us—big bully boys. But we weren't supposed to say so.' Suddenly intense, he was leaning forward, hands on knees. 'Listen, Josie. You must listen to me.'

'Must I?' Here was her chance. She yawned and stretched lasciviously, affecting boredom with the conversation. Up to a point, it was even genuine: surely there was no more to be achieved by wrangling like this? She took her courage in both hands, fixing his gaze with hers—suggestive, sensual. 'I can think of better ways of passing the time, Alex.'

Her innuendo did not escape him. A look of incredulity—almost of distaste—flitted across the strong features; then they hardened again into determination. Choosing not to hear her last remark, he continued in quiet but emphatic tones. 'I admit that when I came along here on Sunday I was checking out the site because of the change of plan. I admit I was in favour of it. I still am—in some ways.' His eyes were directly challenging now, meeting hers unwaveringly. 'I have a job to do, a reputation to maintain. But . . .' he paused here; obviously it was a big 'but'. 'It became clear to me pretty quickly that you had no idea at all what was due to happen. When I came back, I was on the point of telling you—warning you—we knew how you'd feel, Vicky and I—and then . . .'

'How kind of you both!' Josie sneered. Then she took a step towards him, hands on hips. Okay, so she was only wearing her working jeans—but she didn't suppose that would put him off. 'Look Alex,' she pressed on, rather breathless now, 'I'm not really very interested in all this. What good will it all do— explanations, excuses, post mortems?' She injected her tone and expression with as much flirtatious non-chalance as she could muster. 'Last night you made it obvious enough what you wanted from me. But last night it didn't happen to suit me.' It was increasingly hard to keep the tremor from her voice, but she conquered it. 'I'm here now, though, and so are you, and all this isn't getting us anywhere, and—well,' she broke off to summon up a low, sexy laugh, 'I'm not fighting now.'

She could hardly have laid it on the line more blatantly than that. She took another step nearer so that she almost touched him. Secretly, her breath was bated: how would he react? Would he fall into the trap?

Gazing into her face, he shook his head slightly, and she thought she detected a fleeting expression of acute solemnity—even sadness—in his eyes. Then his brows lifted, and his mouth twitched; and his hand reached out to grab her wrist. Her response to his skin against hers was far greater than she had expected, and she very nearly chickened out and backed away. But she regained her control. The tactics were going to work; this was the time to brazen them out.

'All right, Josie. If that's how you want to play it.' His eyes had narrowed. A coldly calculating note had crept into his voice—an element of threat which almost knocked her off guard. 'I certainly didn't come here tonight for . . . that. I thought you'd have other things on your mind today.' His gaze—overtly hungry now—

travelled the length and breadth of her, lingering, appreciating. 'It seems I misjudged you altogether, Miss Barnes, M.A.—you're a tough little number in ways I never imagined. You really had me fooled last night,' he mused—and there was resentment beneath the studied dry humour. 'All that wriggling and protesting; the virginal reluctance to ask me in ...' His fingers tightened, harsh around her wrist.

'I told you, I was tired.' She tossed her head, consciously coquettish. The flutter of eyelashes, the coy grin, emerged as more of a simper. 'It's a lady's prerogative to say no, isn't it?'

Suddenly, in the midst of this ancient ritual, she felt sickened and degraded as she never had before. It was not working. Something was going wrong. The feelings between them were all wrong. In fact, that was the trouble: there were not supposed to be any feelings between them at all. But what was the point in kidding herself? On her side, at least, that just was not true.

She was near to panic, but it was too late to back down now. He was watching her closely, with that probing, alarming shrewdness—which desire did nothing to cloud. She wished desperately she had never embarked on this empty charade.

But he was drawing her inexorably to him, so that she stood between his muscular legs; then he tightened his knees until she was pinned painfully to the spot. Both hands came up to grip her just below the elbows. She was paralysed.

'So,' he drawled, 'it was just so much feminine fuss and bother, was it? The old no-meaning-yes routine? I must say, Josie, I didn't have you labelled as a little tease. I credited you with more—integrity than that.'

'I'm not ... I mean ...' She was all but blushing—a thing she never, ever did.

Without warning he jerked her down so that she was actually sitting in his lap. Then he slid a long arm around her small waist, while the other hand got busy—

briskly cool and efficient, with no preamble—unbutton-
ing her blouse. She gasped, coping with a flood of
responses which were not just unaccustomed; they were
totally new. Ridiculous, adolescent clanging bells in the
ears; flashing lights strobing in her head . . . she had to
pull herself together, get back in charge of the situation.
She had to, before it was too late.

But Alex's superior strength was not, apparently,
confined to the physical level. He was calling the tune—
and he knew it. In the businesslike act of dealing with her
shirt buttons, he caught sight of the square digital watch
on his hair-roughened wrist. Without even the blink of
an eye to indicate a shift of mood, he was on his feet,
decanting her unceremoniously to the floor beside him.
Stepping back from her, he declared calmly: 'Good of you
to make the offer, Josie, but I've got another
appointment. I said I'd be at Vicky's by eight-thirty—to
have supper, talk things over. I'd hoped to square one or
two points with you first—to be honest I rather expected
you to be spoiling for a fight. Naturally I'm glad you're
not, but I can't stop for anything else, I'm afraid. Another
time, maybe.' His tone was politely offhand. They might
have been talking about a cup of coffee.

'That's quite okay, Alex.' It was a nightmare, but she
clung to her poise. Her calculations had gone
catastrophically wrong—exactly how, she had yet to
work out. She buttoned her shirt with shaky fingers.
Perhaps all she could do now was to return to the real
bone of contention. *Spoiling for a fight* . . . well, she
was, wasn't she? If she couldn't deal with him her way,
she would have to resort to good old healthy rage. 'I
suppose,' she conjectured caustically, 'you'll be at this
meeting on Friday?'

'Sure, we'll be there. And you?' He was so detached,
so cool. She hated him.

'If I can get away—can't just abandon things here,
you know. Trivial though our work is, we have to get
on with it—while we're allowed to.'

He was shrugging into his jacket. 'Right. See you there, then, perhaps?'

She made a last-ditch attempt to penetrate his complacency. 'I suppose you don't get paid for your part in this luxury development till it's virtually complete?'

'Not more than a proportion, no,' he agreed mildly, hands in pockets, the top of his head scarcely half an inch from the caravan ceiling.

'So it would be in your best interests to get it up as soon as possible? For—professional and financial reasons?' She tried to make it sound scathing, accusing.

'Certainly,' he acknowledged tersely, one eyebrow arching just a little. 'I never denied it.' *So what*, his tone implied.

Even this was not working out the way she had intended. There never had been such an hour of backfired intentions. 'So,' she concluded desperately, 'there was never any point in you pretending you were concerned for anyone but yourself in all this.'

'No.' He walked to the door, turning the collar of his jacket up against the wind which could now be heard working itself up outside. One hand on the door handle, he swung round. Incredibly, he was smiling. Warm, sincere, it was the final, subtle blow in the face of Josie's bitterness. She could only stare across at him, blank, exposed.

'As a matter of fact, Josie, I can guess how you must be feeling,' Alex announced steadily. 'And I can guess why you did—what you did tonight. But I've already explained to you that I don't much relish the notion of one human being taking sexual advantage of another. To me, sex represents all sorts of things—even a weapon, occasionally, in the battle of the genders, if you like . . . but not—definitely not—a way of avoiding real communication or contact.' He was serious now, but his features were still in their softened mould. 'As to this other business; try not to let it get you down too much. There may yet be a way round. Nothing's ever as cut and dried as it seems. No one's interests are ever as clearly. defined as you seem to think. There are solutions to most problems, compromises in most situations, if you care enough to look for them. I came here this evening to explain and to reassure you that all isn't yet entirely lost. You haven't given me much of a chance to do either. Now I've got to go. End of lecture.' He grinned, completing the disarming process. Then he opened the door. 'Don't despair, Josie. And,' he added thoughtfully, his dark glance flickering warmly across her face, 'despise me—despise men—as much as you like. But try not to despise yourself too much. You don't deserve it.'

Before she could formulate a single word, Alex was gone—merging with the darkness. She stood stock-still, ears strained for the sound of the jeep as it swished and roared away. Then there was just silence, and the whine of the wind—and a distinct impression that she had been turned upside down and inside out and given a thorough, yet strangely gentle, shaking up.

She was far too tired and upset to work out the complications which seemed to have tangled her life up. She put herself to bed very early, falling into a stunned doze: but all night his face haunted her dreams, hard and then kind—fierce and then concerned; his voice, with its Scottish lilt, loomed and faded through her recent memory. *Nothing's as cut and dried as it seems. Compromises ... solutions ... if you care enough. Try not to despise yourself ...*

The whole thing was crazy. Next day, she would come to her senses again, be her practical, dependable self. Simon would be there to help her to sort some of it out. The rest of it—well, she would have to fight back to her customary spirit. All that righteous indignation had not deserted her; it had just given way, temporarily, to some peculiar weakness. Everything would be back to normal—in the morning.

CHAPTER FIVE

It was a difficult day, to say the least. Whichever direction her thoughts tried to turn, her stomach churned and her throat constricted. It took every bit of her self-control not to give way and break down; but she managed it.

She thought she had never been so pleased to see anything as Simon's battered Morris Minor when it chugged into sight about tea time. She ran to greet him as he unfolded his rangy, bejeaned form from behind the wheel.

An old friend from student days—sandy-haired, bespectacled, laconic—Simon was one of the few people in the world with whom she felt really at ease. They worked together well, and they understood each other well; and there was never the slightest question or threat of something more, because he had lived with the same girl—a primary school teacher—for three years. Simon and Claire were, in fact, everyone's model of domestic contentment and fidelity.

He sprawled in a chair now, while Josie put the kettle on, regarding her from thoughtful grey eyes; but he said nothing until she turned to face him, meeting his glance directly for the first time. Then he offered her an encouraging smile, and she managed a watery one in return.

'What's up, Jo?' Simon never used ten words where three would do.

She pulled a wry face. 'Is it that obvious?'

'I know you better than most people,' he reminded her gently. 'You look like someone who's lost a pound and found a penny—or seen your own ghost,' he remarked, his mild gaze resting on her tense features.

She sighed deeply. 'That's not a bad description of how I feel.' She turned away from him to make the tea as the kettle came to the boil behind her.

'Want to tell me about it? Or is it too personal?'

'Don't worry.' Her grin was dry and humourless. 'You're doomed to hear all about it, whether you want to or not. No, it's not personal—at least, not . . .' She faltered, tightening her lips, narrowing her eyes. 'No,' she repeated vehemently, 'it's not personal. It's professional.'

His pale eyebrows lifted. 'Sounds bad. And you were on such a high when you phoned. Something wrong about these skeletons? Graves turn out to be modern after all? It's happened before.' He peered closely at her. 'Your trainees haven't been playing tricks on you?'

'Good lord, no, nothing like that. The skeletons are lovely, and so are the trainees. They've dug up five so far, and I'm willing to bet there are plenty more. I've stopped them digging for the moment, till you've had a good look—but it was all I could do to persuade them to take a break, they're so keen.' Josie's face softened. 'I expect they'll be in soon to have a cup of tea with you.'

'Well, if it's all looking so rosy—what's wrong?' he pressed.

Josie sat down, setting two steaming mugs on the table. Acutely aware, all at once, of how worn out she felt, she rubbed her eyes with the thumb and finger of one hand in a gesture he recognised; then pushed her thick auburn hair back off her face. 'Everything,' she declared dolefully.

He frowned. 'Doesn't just sound bad—sounds terminal. Since when?'

'Since yesterday. And terminal is about the right word.' She laughed—briefly, sardonically, at the back of her throat. 'A very good word for it.'

He took an appreciative swig of tea. 'You'd better get if off your chest, Josie, before your gang invade us.

From what I remember, when they take over this place they don't do it by halves.'

'You're too right.' She expelled another profound sigh, almost a yawn, which seemed to start somewhere around her ankles. 'And I haven't told them yet.'

'Told them what?' He was patiently persistent, sensing a need for tact.

For answer she reached into a back pocket of her denims and pulled out the evidence—somewhat tattered and crumpled now, but none the less incriminating for all that. It should, she reflected as she handed it to him in silence, have a black border round it.

He studied it intently—reading each line carefully, then going back to the beginning to re-read the whole thing as if he hoped to penetrate between the lines as well. Then he looked up, folding the letter as he disgested its contents. 'Hmmm,' he said.

'You might well say "Hmmm". Personally, I found a few choicer phrases came to mind when I first read it,' she observed bitterly.

'I can imagine.' He opened the sheet again and had another look. Then he shook his head, clicking his tongue in disapproval. Being placid by nature, that was about as worked up over anything as Simon usually became. 'I suppose they must be within their legal rights? I mean, wouldn't they have signed an agreement not to continue work before a certain period? How long did you specify in the first place?'

'Two years minimum. I thought of that too—but can you see a massive firm like this slipping up on its legal obligations? No, I'm afraid they're much too slick for that. They'll have the best advice—like they do about everything.' The wry aside was lost on Simon. 'I'll get the Commission and the Council to check up, of course; but I'm afraid we won't get them that way.'

He was still staring at the letter, thinking it through. 'Anyway, I expect this magic three months covers them for that.'

'Just what I decided.' She brooded into her mug of tea. 'The bastards!' she exclaimed, overcome yet again by the scale of this corporate betrayal.

His glance was sympathetic as he spread the offending document on the table between them. 'Poor Jo. Just when it was all going so well.'

From anyone else she might have reacted scathingly to this rather trite comment; but there was one thing you could be sure of with Simon—he always meant exactly what he said. Understatement was his natural form of expression.

She shrugged. 'I'll fight it, of course. I'll take them on single-handed if necessary. They won't get away with it—not without a battle.'

He stared vaguely at a point just above her head, and his mouth twitched. 'I bet they won't. Not with Spitfire Barnes to contend with. I could almost feel sorry for them,' he added wickedly.

Feeling a bit better, she stuck out her tongue at him. Simon was such a comfort—like a favourite, well-worn garment. Thank goodness she had already sent for him on other business before this thing had hit her. Needing a friend around at such a time was, surely, a sign of weakness—she should have been able to cope with it on her own. 'Don't waste your pity on those . . . robots. There isn't a human being among them—just cogs and wheels.' Her green eyes sparked scorn.

'Are you so sure?' he mused. 'There must be someone you can get on to your side? How about their outside advisers—planners, designers, that sort of thing?' She said nothing, so he went on. 'Sometimes those people do have a sense of history—or at least a feeling for the environment—which is entirely lacking in your more blatant capitalist developer.' She remained silent, so he expanded his theme a bit further. 'Self-interest might still be uppermost, but it might be just a little more enlightened. Had you thought of contacting anyone like that?'

Her gaze focussed on to the active scene outside the window. 'As it happens, I've made the acquaintance of two—what did you call them?—"outside advisers" only recently. Architects. To be precise, the big chief architect and his illustrious colleague, the landscape designer. They were good enough to honour us with their presence, sussing out the site, preparing the ground for action, girding their loins.'

'And?' He was studying her closely, elbows leaning on the table-top.

'And what?' She faced him, unconsciously squaring her slim shoulders.

'Well—were they sympathetic? Could you get them on to your side?'

'Oh, they made noises about how impressive it all was—everything we're doing.'

'Well then. Any ally is better than none,' Simon pointed out practically. 'Why don't you enlist their help, get them to . . .'

'No, Simon.' Her tone, hard and flat, warned him off the subject. 'They're all in it together. It's in their best interests to get the houses up as fast as possible. Whatever they want us to think. Acting all turned-on, bringing their kids along . . .' her fists clenched in renewed distress as her tone rose and tightened.

'Hey there, calm down, Jo,' he soothed, used to her temperamental reactions. 'I'm sure it was nothing personal, if they seemed . . .'

'You can say that again. Nothing personal.' Her laugh was hollow and painful. 'And if he thought he could manipulate me he's got another think coming.'

'He?' Simon quirked a puzzled eyebrow. He sensed complications, but for the moment he was out of his depth.

'This architect. Grant, his name is, Alexander Grant. Local big shot in the trade. Dynamic, go-getting, award-winning—you know the type.'

'Ah.' Simon nodded blandly. 'And you say he brought a colleague? What about him?'

'Her. Vicky Randle. She seemed rather nice, actually,' Josie said wistfully. 'Even brought her children. A family day out, at our expense . . .' she groaned.

'Josie, you've got to keep your cool over this. Try to stay objective. I know it's not easy, but it's your only hope. Don't get personally involved.' He could not possibly have known how apposite this advice was, and she did not tell him. 'Will you be going to this meeting tomorrow? I think you should, if you can.'

'If you can stay here and keep an eye on things?'

'Sure—glad to be useful. Looks like I've arrived at an opportune moment. When I left Cambridge this morning, I didn't realise what I was getting into,' he teased.

'How long can you stay?'

'A few days, no problem. After that my students just might start noticing I'm not there.' He grinned. 'Not to mention Claire.'

'Don't worry, I won't detain you from her too long. But I must admit I'm glad to have you here just now, Si. Will you be okay sleeping in here, like last time?'

'Sure will—it's very cosy. I've got my sleeping bag. I'll be fine.' He stood up and stretched, his hands easily reaching the ceiling. 'Now, if you don't mind, I must answer a call of nature and then get a breath of fresh air. It was a long drive.'

'Oh Simon, I'm sorry.' She shook her head ruefully. 'I haven't even asked you how Claire is, or anything, I've been so preoccupied with my problems.'

'Don't be silly. She's fine. The drive was fine. The old bus chugs along. The car, that is, not Claire.'

They both laughed. 'It's good to have you here,' she said again. Then she looked out of the window. 'Watch out—the mob's advancing. Make yourself at home while I put the kettle on again. When you've been formally welcomed, you'll be dragged off to admire their finds. Mustn't forget why you're actually here.'

'No way.' Simon was already heading for the inner cabin. 'Mustn't forget that.'

'But don't forget,' she called after him, 'they don't know the news yet. Whatever you do, don't let it out. It'll cause a revolution. I've got to be ready.'

'Sure thing, boss,' Simon said, closing the interconnecting door behind him.

Wallace Holdings housed itself in a rigidly symmetrical, oblong edifice, entirely constructed, as far as Josie could see, from metal and glass. Despite being near the centre of Bristol, where space was at a premium, it boasted its own car park and even a patch of ground, carefully laid out to look as spacious and verdant as possible. As she pulled into a small space between two large, ostentatious Jaguars, Josie found herself wondering whether Grant Randle Holt had had a hand in it anywhere. Surely Alex could not have designed anything so ugly? Judging by what she remembered of the plans for the Summerford site, his style was infinitely more subtle and understated.

Pulling her thoughts firmly to order, she set off across the courtyard to the imposing entrance with its twin revolving doors. She had worked hard to produce a neatly efficient image for the occasion: the flared, flecked tweed skirt and matching jacket which hugged her trim curves, the knee-high natural leather boots and long-strapped shoulder bag. There wasn't much she could do about taming her fine auburn mane, but she had brushed it fiercely into some semblance of order before she left. Under her left arm, completing the picture of smart professionalism, she carried a flat briefcase.

The reception lobby was predictably vast, and liberally furnished in plastic and chrome. Her heels sank into an inch of green carpet (a colour chosen, she suspected, because it was supposed to be restful, though to her eye it looked bilious). The smiles on the two flawlessly-painted faces behind the long white reception desk were surely fixed there permanently with the same glue they used to attach their eyelashes?

The Chairman's Suite, up on the fifth floor, turned out to be a series of offices, complete with the same green carpet and several pretty young secretaries. Then there was an inner office with an even deeper, gold carpet and a more mature, brisk secretary. Finally, Josie was shown into the holy of holies: the Boardroom itself, the heart of the company, where rank outsiders and lower orders rarely penetrated. Josie wondered if she should fall on her knees and kiss the ankle-deep, red carpet. Instead she simply sat quietly in the polished wooden chair she was directed to at the foot of an enormous oval table, and concentrated on sorting out her papers—refusing to look up and meet the roomful of curious eyes she could sense turned in her direction.

'Miss Barnes,' the secretary announced in an apologetic tone to those present.

'Thank you, Miss Harris.' The smooth male voice, with its faultless well-bred accents, carried clearly from the top end of the table. 'Good-afternoon to you, Miss Barnes. So pleased you could spare the time from your worthy activities to join our little gathering.'

Then, and only then, Josie looked up and allowed her cool gaze to take in the scene. There were, perhaps, ten men seated at the table—although she guessed it could easily have accommodated fifty. Every place was tidily set—as if for a banquet, she thought with a stab of amusement, with blotters and pads for plates and mats, pens and pencils for cutlery, even sparkling cut-glass tumblers and jugs of water to lubricate the process of high-powered discussion. She had heard and read about this sort of thing, of course—who had not?—but it felt crazily unreal to be thrown in among it, even temporarily. She was a working girl, an outdoor girl. She needed action and fresh air, not sitting about in stuffy boardrooms.

And stuffy it was, in spite of its wide, high-ceilinged dimensions and the smell of furniture polish. The pollution was mainly due, she soon realised, to the fact that several of her fellow-delegates were smoking fat cigars; and most of those who were not clutched cigarettes. Josie shuddered inwardly; she resented it deeply, being forced to inhale other people's cast-off fumes. Never mind what it was doing to them—that was their own decision, after all; what about the nasty things it was doing to *her*?

However, this was hardly the moment to dwell on such private preoccupations; she was here for a purpose. Across acres of mahogany, she faced the man who had addressed her, ignoring the others. 'Good-afternoon,' she returned stiffly. 'I wouldn't have dreamed of missing it,' she replied to his second facetious comment.

Middle-aged and exceedingly well-fed, he leaned back in his extra-large chair at the head of the table. In common with all his colleagues, he was dressed in one of those impeccable pinstriped suits she had imagined gracing the frame of the minion who had dealt with her on the phone. It was all she could do to stifle a smirk as she registered their uniform, differing only in the basic choice of dark blue, grey, brown or black between the stripes. They were doubtless all decent, ordinary men, she reminded herself—with wives and children at home, kind to their poor old mothers, rescuers of stray dogs, upholders of liberty, subscribers to charities. Somehow, it didn't seem to help.

'I wish everyone concerned had been equally conscientious,' drawled the voice from the top end of the table. Through the haze, she could just discern watery eyes—pale but keen, summing her up far more intently than his laconic manner revealed. 'Your enthusiasm does you credit, Miss Barnes—eh, gentlemen?'

His yes-men nodded eagerly, displaying a sudden

dutiful interest in the nondescript young woman. Josie
wondered which of them, if any, she had been
privileged to speak to on the telephone. Probably
someone too insignificant to attend a Special Meeting
such as this.

'Yes,' he went on, still staring at her thoughtfully. 'We
have received apologies from the Commission, as well as
the Council. It seems they do not see fit to send
representatives to this little gathering, although they have
expressed profound concern as to its outcome. You
appear to be sole pleader for your cause, Miss Barnes.'

That was a body-blow, and he knew it; but Josie
refused to flinch. She held her head high. 'I dare say
they regard it as a foregone conclusion, from bitter
experience,' she retorted boldly—her clear voice
echoing down the room. 'But I don't give up so easily.'

His eyes narrowed; he took a puff of his cigar.
'Alarming opposition, gentlemen,' he remarked to his
colleagues, a cruel edge of satire in his tone.

There was sycophantic laughter from all sides. Josie
fought the flush which threatened to give her anger and
embarrassment away. She must keep her outer poise at
all costs. This was not going to be easy—that much was
obvious; but she had faced challenges before. It took
more than a few pompous directors to unsettle her.

Mercifully, before she could find a suitable reply,
their attention was distracted by several new arrivals—
mainly men, all apparently from the same pinstriped
clone, but Josie was irrationally glad to see two women
among them. Groomed and permed almost beyond
recognition they might be, but at least she had some
female company. They all sat together, as close to the
magic throne as they could get, heads turned to its
occupant, ears strained for his every comment. The
Chairman held court—confident, relaxed, to the
manner born. Much to Josie's relief, none of them took
any more notice of her. The room already swirled
through its pall of smoke.

Eventually the redoubtable Miss Harris took her place beside the Chairman (but in a much smaller chair), preparing herself to take copious notes and generally keep everyone in order. She coughed tactfully. 'Er . . . Mr Chairman, ladies and gentlemen, if you would care to begin this Special Meeting of the Board . . . we are ten minutes late already . . .'

'But we aren't all here.' Looking pained, the Chairman stubbed his half-finished cigar out in a large glass ashtray. 'What about the architects? They made enough fuss about being present.' He glared accusingly at Miss Harris—and so did Josie, who had been trying not to wonder much the same thing, though for mixed and different reasons. 'Don't tell me they've backed out too?'

The other delegates immediately started muttering darkly to each other, causing a rustle of disapproval among which Josie could make out phrases like 'Disgraceful!' and 'Can't trust these chaps!'

Miss Harris tapped unhappily on the table with her notebook. 'They said they would be here, Sir, but I don't think we should wait indefinitely. You all have other important appointments to keep after this . . .'

'Hear, hear!' agreed the assembled company.

'Very well then.' The Chairman sat forward—alert now, businesslike, a self-important figurehead swinging into decisive action. 'Let's get on with it.'

Miss Harris cleared her throat again. 'The purpose of this Special Meeting is to allow extra discussion of the proposal to bring forward the date of resumption of construction work on the site for residential development at Summerford. As you will all be aware, this was not scheduled to begin again for another year, after being shelved for a two-year period when it was discovered that . . .'

At this point, the door opened and a flustered young secretary ushered in two more delegates. Without even looking round, Josie sensed immediately that one of them was Alex; and she stiffened herself for the inevitable confrontation. As soon as he entered the room she felt his impact—and it reduced these other characters to the status of fools and clowns; there was no getting away from it.

The familiar voice, from disconcertingly close behind her, vibrated across the silence—quietly firm. 'I do apologise for our late arrival, Chairman. Mrs Randle and I have been conducting some last-minute researches, hoping to be able to bring a new point of discussion to this meeting. Unfortunately we were delayed in traffic on the way back. We hope we haven't inconvenienced you.'

The Chairman inclined his head graciously. 'As you see Mr Grant—Mrs Randle—we had started without you. Please be seated,' he invited, coldly polite. There was no love lost, Josie noted, between Alex and the Chairman of the Board. She wondered why.

Alex and Vicky sat down at Josie's end of the table—but not too uncomfortably close to her. Vicky caught her eye and sent her a quick grin. Alex held her glance for a long, penetrating moment before turning away to consult his notes. Something in his expression—a brooding grimness—caused Josie's stomach to clench in a way that no boardroom full of portly chairmen and managing directors could ever do. He was dressed exactly as usual, in slim casual cords and a soft cotton shirt open at the throat—and looked more of a man, in Josie's reluctant opinion, than all the rest put together. The only shirt present, her mind quipped wickedly, which was not stuffed.

The Chairman's level gaze directed itself on to Alex. 'And did you achieve any further points of discussion?' he enquired stiffly.

Alex returned the gaze without a flicker. 'Not exactly.' His lips tightened. From where she sat, two or three seats away, Josie could see his classic, bearded profile, exuding—what? annoyance? frustration? She was puzzled: there were undercurrents here she was not sure she understood.

'Well, if you're quite ready,' the Chairman suggested heavily, 'perhaps we might have another bash at getting this meeting under way?'

'Certainly.' Alex was presenting that new, uncompromising face she had so suddenly confronted a few uncomfortable hours earlier. His public—or was it his real?—self: calm, controlled—and yet mercilessly tough and razor-sharp. A grim, unbending, formidable opponent. Yet another good reason for wishing fervently that they were on the same side in this business.

Now Miss Harris was patiently calling the meeting to order all over again. Once formalities were dispensed with—minutes read, the agenda defined—the Chairman condescendingly put the case as the company saw it.

Naturally, he claimed, this decision was deeply regretted; but apparently it was inevitable. Their hands were tied. The building contractors had left them no option. As everyone was only too well aware, prices were rising every day—labour prices, material prices; unless they resumed work on the site within three months, the originally estimated cost of the development would escalate out of all proportion. The contractors were waiting to start on other schemes, and might even back out altogether if not allowed to get going soon. And heaven knew what *that* might do to the overall cost! He wished to remind the meeting, in all modesty, that the contractors had been highly unwilling to agree to the postponement of the development in the first place. It had taken all his own personal diplomacy to persuade them.

Certainly, he added as an afterthought, some useful archaeological finds had been made in the last year, as he understood it—and he hoped they would all remember (and here he looked significantly in Josie's direction) that these had taken place in time that was

already borrowed from the firm's construction work
schedule . . .

Josie listened to his complacent words with growing
fury. It was an effort to keep her lips tightly
compressed, preventing the escape of any scathing
reactions. The last thing her case needed was
uncontrolled, disorderly behaviour. She must show the
meeting she was a force to be taken seriously. She kept
her head well down, refusing to meet anyone's glance,
even Vicky's anxiously sympathetic one. She knew her
opportunity to speak would come—if she proved she
could abide by the rules.

After the Chairman had outlined the proposition,
several of his henchmen rose to endorse it. They were a
tight, well-rehearsed team. With each speaker, Josie's
heart sank further: her original suspicion had been
right—there was no redress against this powerful band
of self-interest. Every query, every objection she had
come along planning to raise—they were all being
systematically shot down before she had even been
given the chance to say a word.

The firm's legal spokesman then informed the
meeting that they were well within their statutory rights
and obligations—as long as they allowed the three
months' notice which had been duly given. He sent
round copies of the initial agreement which had
specified this, with the relevant passage of small print
underlined in red in case anyone missed it. Josie—who
had missed it when she first read it—cursed herself. Not
that she could have done much about it even if she had
spotted it, she had left all that side of things to her
sponsors and funding agents; and a fat lot of help they
were turning out to be!

A representative of the building contractors themselves clarified their own position, which had already
(he said), been so succinctly described by the Chairman.
Economic stringencies . . . financial difficulties . . .
everyone knew what hard times we lived in.

Unfortunately, sacrifices had to be made in the interests of progress.

Sacrifices! Josie's mind taunted—so loudly that she was sure the sound must be coming out of her ears. She doubted whether many people in this room would recognise a sacrifice if you were to ram one down their throats. If sacrifices had to be made, one thing was certain: her fellow-delegates were not going to be the ones who made them.

Miss Harris then explained that she had received messages from the local Council who sponsored Josie's Project, and from the Commission which had funded it. Both had expressed regret at being unable to attend this meeting. ('Cowards! Traitors!' sang Josie's mind.) Both bodies had at first been extremely put out at the news, mainly because a team of young unemployed people had been successfully learning a new trade on the Project.

'Well,' the Chairman pointed out lazily, 'it keeps them off the streets.' Amid the general mirth which greeted this remark, Josie allowed herself the barest glimmer of hope: perhaps her sponsors were not going to let her down after all.

But, Miss Harris continued, they had since been much reassured by the news that new jobs would be found, within the Commission's Training Scheme, for each and every one of these young trainees—as apprentice plasterers, bricklayers and so on.

Josie could hardly contain her rage. So that was it! Her so-called allies had sold out completely—for the price of a few cheap jobs! But what about the kids themselves—her own workers, whose imaginations had been so wonderfully captivated by this new world they were discovering? Whose whole personalities were changing before her very eyes, as they became absorbed in the miracle of digging up the past? To suggest that it would be all the same to them if they were asked to dig foundations and build brick walls instead! She seethed;

she gritted her teeth; but still she kept her head down, avoiding any amused glances which came her way.

'And I'm sure louts like that will hardly care,' the Chairman saw fit to observe, as if reading her smarting thoughts, 'what they have to do to get their twenty-five quid a week, as long as they get it.' The meeting—or a large part of it—giggled appreciatively at his penetrating wit.

Then the Chairman turned to Alex and Vicky. 'I don't know if our architects wish to add anything to what has been said?' Again, Josie detected that faint note of warning behind the suave tones. 'Mr Grant has been behind us in this decision since its earliest stages,' he pointed out blandly. 'It was he, in fact, who made the original suggestion to the Board that, since costs were soaring every day, things might perhaps be speeded up. I believe you told us, did you not Mr Grant, that you might otherwise be forced to modify your designs in order to keep the total price even reasonably close to original estimates?'

At this confirmation of her worst suspicions, Josie's veneer of calm very nearly cracked open completely. She had known it all along—Alex had been against her from the start; but to have it brought home so starkly— it was almost more than she could bear. She clenched her fists on her lap, hating him.

But he was getting to his feet; slowly, deliberately, taking his time. His dark glance ranged round the meeting for a moment, coming to rest on Josie's face. For a weak second she allowed herself to look straight at him—and wished she hadn't. How could those brown eyes still be as warm, as direct, even as they sparked this new stony determination? How could they still have this effect on her, even now that she knew the truth?

Vicky sat quietly at his side, looking up at him like everyone else. Alex had presence, it had to be admitted. Unlike all the other speakers (including the Chairman), he commanded a natural, rather than an artificial, respect.

'Mr Chairman.' His voice was low but confident. 'Ladies and gentlemen. All I wish to say is this. My partners and I did, originally, endorse this proposal to resume construction work on the Summerford site nine months early. It made a lot of economic sense—not least for our own firm. The longer the delay, the more the profits are eaten away by inflation. We are as concerned as anyone else to maintain financial efficiency.'

The Wallace Holdings representatives nodded and smiled at one another. He was talking their language. The Chairman looked slightly surprised. Vicky stared down at her hands. Josie kept her gaze fixed on the wall in front of her, fighting back tears which were nearer than tears had a right to be—especially in public.

'But,' Alex drew their attention again, 'there are, generally speaking, two sides to such a case.' There was a short, frigid silence. The Chairman pursed up his lips and shook his head. Vicky continued to look at her hands, and Josie to stare at the wall. 'We expressed these opinions,' Alex went on emphatically, 'before we had had a chance to revisit the site itself.' His eyes were focussed on to the Chairman now. 'As soon as the decision became official, I felt it necessary to do just that. My partner, Mrs Randle, came with me.' He glanced briefly at Vicky, who still did not look up. Obviously she was finding all this difficult. Josie herself hardly knew what to feel; a strange conflict of emotions surged through her—hope and cynicism, relief and despair.

'What we saw in operation there—the success, the scale and validity of the whole thing—impressed us deeply,' Alex told them simply. 'I put it to you, ladies and gentlemen: if you were to go to Summerford, see for yourselves the discoveries that have been made, I feel sure you would know what we mean. There are times when economic considerations might be asked to give way to wider, longer-term priorities; and this, I venture to suggest, is one of those times.'

He stood tall, pausing to let this sink in. Then, into a horrified silence, he spoilt it all by concluding: 'Having said all that, we cannot retract our earlier advice that any delay will inevitably cause further rises in costs—including our own. For this reason we had hoped to come up with a compromise today—in fact, we arrived late this afternoon because we had been involved in a highly complex discussion with our colleagues, the contractors, to see if something couldn't be worked out to suit everyone.' His heavy brows met in a bleak frown. 'It would seem not.' Then he sat down, and the only sound was the rustling of Miss Harris's papers.

The Chairman reached in his breast pocket for another fat cigar, which he rolled carefully between thumb and third finger as if for reassurance. Then he gazed down the table at Alex. 'Well, Mr Grant,' he said slowly. 'I had been informed that you were having second thoughts on your original recommendation, so I can't pretend to be surprised. As to your quaint invitation to us to visit the site: I suspect most of us are far too busy to go tramping across muddy fields, poking into goodness knows what ancient remains, for the good of our souls . . . so we will accept your word that the findings are impressive.' He paused theatrically for the inevitable laughter.

'Regrettably,' he went on, his tone hardening, 'we are not in a position to allow such sentimental motives to sway us from our chosen path. We have duly noted your new stance, Mr Grant—and also the fact that you remain basically, in essence, fully in support of the proposal. In fact, as I have said, your advice was instrumental in our reaching the decision in the first place.' He held the cigar to his nose and sniffed at it approvingly. 'I have no idea what this . . . compromise might be which you saw fit to try and concoct, but I do assure you, Mr Grant, that if there had been a way out which might have preserved the Project, we would have found it.'

Like hell you would, Josie's mind intoned. Her faintly stirring hopes crashed even lower than they had been before. Alex had just been blustering, of course, like the rest of them. His pretty speech had been so much window dressing for her benefit, he knew perfectly well it would make no difference in the end; he could afford to take a brief stand on her behalf, secure in the knowledge that no one would pay the least attention to it . . . that the Chairman would shoot it down in flames.

And now it was her turn. She stood to address the meeting—last on the list, the end of the line, alone in the defence area. Aware that they were all looking at her expectantly, she drew a deep breath and stared at a point above Miss Harris's head.

'I realise, Mr Chairman,' she began calmly, 'that absolutely nothing I might say here today is going to make any difference to your decision. This meeting is a—a farce,' she declared boldly. 'It's no more than cynical lip-service to the democratic process. You had it well sewn-up before any of us got here. You've successfully bought off my sponsors and financing agents with your promises of full placements for my trainees within your own scheme.' She swallowed hard, willing herself to stay cool. 'If you did come and see those youngsters in action, I think you'd see that Mr Grant was right.' The way his name fell from her lips in that natural, spontaneous flow! If they did but know what it cost her to say it! 'They are becoming keen, involved, in some cases skilled, budding archaeologists. It's an old, a vital, an exciting trade.' Her voice lifted, her face became animated as she warmed to the subject. 'There is no way,' she assured them earnestly, 'most of those kids will want to be transferred to some soulless piece of building work. It's nothing short of insulting to suggest that they won't know the difference.'

She glanced down at her notes, gathering herself together. That was enough of that: she would only put their backs up still further if she said more. But what was the point in going on—was it flogging a dead horse?

With a supreme effort, she listed her major finds, culminating in a description of the graves, pointing out that many more might remain undiscovered for all time as a result of today's decision.

'All we might learn from our ancestors,' she told them, as unemotionally as possible, 'is wrapped up under the ground in places like that. And if you proceed with this ... this reversal of your original commitment,' she challenged heatedly, 'you will take full responsibility for depriving future generations of valuable knowledge.'

She sat down abruptly, again to a short silence. Catching her eye, Vicky raised an eyebrow as if in agreement. Alex was staring at her too—her whole body told her that; but she averted her gaze firmly from his. The last thing she needed at this moment was any direct contact with the man.

The Chairman had got out his cigar-cutter and was performing minor surgery on his Havana. His yes-men waited with baited breath to see which way the cookie would crumble. Josie—who knew there was not a cat's chance in hell that it would go her way—started trembling, now that it was all over bar the shouting.

'Well, Miss Barnes,' he spoke at last, his ample frame settling expansively back in its chair. 'You have plucked our heart-strings with your impassioned plea, and I'm sure we all feel nothing but sympathy. We do assure you, as we have all along, that this change of policy was reached only after the most careful and detailed consideration. You have already, it seems, employed your persuasive powers to entice our illustrious architects to your way of thinking—or very nearly.' He smiled dangerously. *Far too nearly for our liking*, the smile said. 'But I'm afraid, in the last analysis, when all's said and done, we must face hard facts.'

The meeting nodded and murmured its agreement. We've had our fun, Josie thought bitterly; now the real world has to shove the children out of the way—get rid of their little buckets and spades and move in the grown-up diggers. Construction for some; destruction for others: the way of the world.

'Naturally,' the Chairman's tone was wry, 'in the interests of the . . . democratic process, we shall put the matter to the vote at the end of this meeting. I hope you will agree that every angle has been freely investigated, Miss Barnes, and that everyone has had their say in a frank, fair and uninterrupted exchange of views.'

Josie didn't even bother to reply to this insulting stream of boardroom jargon. It had been a charade from start to finish—Alex's part in it as much as the rest: a convincing show of concern from someone close to the company's interests. In fact she wouldn't be surprised if Wallace Holdings had not put him up to that too—all part of the floor show. Having seen them in action, she wouldn't put anything past any of them.

She shook her head in grim dejection, and suffered fate to take its course. When Miss Harris asked for a show of hands against the proposal, she did not even bother to raise hers. She did not look up to see whether Alex and Vicky were bothering to raise theirs. It was all too ludicrous; she felt empty—drained and empty—dirty and deflated, somehow, like a punctured football.

'Motion carried by an overwhelming majority,' announced Miss Harris happily. 'In the absence of Any Other Business, I now declare this Special Meeting of the Board officially concluded.'

CHAPTER SIX

THERE was just one thought in Josie's spinning head: to get away from that travesty of a meeting—that ridiculous building—as fast and as far as possible. While everyone was yawning, stretching and smugly congratulating themselves on the successful outcome of their manoeuvrings, she gathered her things together and fled. Through the door, through the inner office with its gold carpet, and the outer office with its green carpet, past the efficient secretaries, who blinked up from their typewriters in surprise and into the wide, deserted corridor; pausing only to inhale a lungful of relatively fresh air like a hunted animal before she made for the lifts.

One glance at the dials showed that they were all at the ground floor. Not wanting to wait about while they obeyed her summons, she set off down the staircase at a brisk sprint—propelled by a driving instinct for escape. *From what, exactly?* her mind was busy demanding, somewhere far beneath the surface; but she didn't stop to listen to it, let alone try to answer it. Time enough to work all that out when she was safely away from this dreadful place and all it stood for ... from those dreadful people ... perhaps most of all, from the disconcerting influences of Alexander Grant.

It was no use, of course: she should have known that. Even if she had got physically away, it would have been only a temporary reprieve. Mentally and emotionally she would have been forced to face up to these latest challenges sooner or later. On no level could the last hour's events just be pushed aside and forgotten. They required action—positive, decisive action—and Josie had no idea what she was going to do next.

Somewhere between the fourth and third floors, the immediate future was taken effectively out of her hands. She was light and quick on her feet; but Alex was powerfully agile and his legs were a lot longer. She knew who it was as soon as she heard him descending the flight of stairs just above her. Pulse racing, expression fiercely set, she kept going, but in a matter of seconds he was right behind her.

Her body sensed his hand reaching out to grab her, even before she felt its hard pressure on her shoulder; and still she went on running, subject to some blind, primeval urge to evade the predator. When his grip tightened she was forced to stop short—staring straight ahead, refusing to move until he turned her slowly, inexorably round to face him, flooding her with awareness of his superior size and strength.

Not a syllable passed between them as they stared at each other for a long, frozen moment. It took all Josie's control not to display her nervous reaction. Alex's warm brown eyes were still fiercely hooded, his sensual lips twisted. When he finally spoke, the tone was strangely brittle.

'Where do you think you're running off to, Miss Barnes?'

She struggled to produce a voice that was as near normal as possible. 'I've got to get back. You know I can't leave the dig for too long at a time.' Not too bad: a bit husky, maybe, but cool enough.

But the excuse cut no ice with him. 'Try again, little lady,' he sneered. She wondered yet again what had become of that astutely sensitive man she had sat opposite in the restaurant—three short days, and yet a lifetime, ago . . . opened herself to . . . 'They've done without you this long; they can manage a bit longer. The ancient profession of archaeology won't fall apart without the constant ministrations of Josephine Barnes, M.A. Not even your own private slice of it.'

With both hands firmly planted on her slim

shoulders, he had the advantage of her in more ways than one. He was carrying nothing at all—doubtless having thrown his papers at Vicky before setting off in hot pursuit of his prey—while Josie was encumbered with her various bits of baggage, not to mention her jacket, which she had removed in the stuffy atmosphere of the meeting and which was now flung carelessly over one arm as she made her getaway.

She moved uneasily in his grasp, shifting her briefcase higher up under her right arm with her left hand, almost dropping her jacket in the process. But she kept her head held high, chin defiantly tilted as she met his piercing gaze.

'I never suggested it would. I don't regard myself as that indispensable.'

'I'm relieved to hear it.' His humour was restoring itself now, with a touch of that familiar restrained irony, but his fingers were still tight around her upper arms. She could feel every one of them on her skin, an individual band of steel through the thin cotton of her shirt. 'No one—but no one—is that indispensable. I know how you feel about your young charges, Josie, but you can't spoonfeed them forever. They'll have to learn to cope without Mother Hen sometime.'

'Sooner than we thought, apparently,' she retorted, her anger rising anew as she remembered. 'When you and your cronies have your way . . .'

'Josie,' he cut in—his voice and eyes hardening. 'There are one or two points I think we should clear up between us before we're too much older.' He glanced round: the staircase was deserted—no doubt most of the employees of this well-heeled establishment preferred to use the lifts; but still it felt exposed. 'I don't propose to discuss them here on the landing, so I must insist that you spare me a few minutes of your precious time before you make your break for the wide open spaces.'

Insist, was it? Not *ask*, or *request*, or *suggest* . . . She sighed, too weary and stressed suddenly to argue—and too conscious of her body's treacherous responses to his hands upon it. 'Where did you have in mind then?' she demanded suspiciously.

'I'll show you—if you'll deign to accompany me. Somewhere we can be reasonably private—but not so secluded as to allow for contact of a more ... intimate nature,' he added on a low, sardonic note.

She winced at this pointed, personal barb. 'Let go of me,' she commanded, 'and I might consider coming with you.'

At once he lifted his hands and shoved them deep in his pockets. She was free to go. Reaching one hand up to rub the opposite smarting shoulder, she dropped her gaze to her boots. Her mouth turned ruefully down at the corners: she was not going to run away from him—not now—and he knew it perfectly well. This was one battle that had gone squarely to him. After the other night, she knew she owed it to him to at least listen to what he had to say. She had got out of it then; he was not about to let her get out of it now.

'Okay,' she conceded coldly. 'As long as it doesn't take all day. I really have got to ...'

But he was off ahead of her, up the stairs on the way to the next floor. 'Don't worry,' he turned to fling over his shoulder. 'You're not the only one with heavy pressures on your time. I promised Vicky I'd be back in Bath later this afternoon. We've got plenty to talk over too. At this rate neither of us will get home till well into evening.'

Josie struggled to catch up as he took the steps two at a time. 'Don't let me detain you then,' she panted sarcastically. 'All I want is to get away from here.'

'Don't worry,' he repeated grimly. 'This won't take long.'

Won't take long, Josie's mind echoed. *Won't feel a thing. Nothing to it.* Just like being at the dentist. *This will hurt me more than it hurts you ...*

He strode along another of those endless impersonal

corridors of power—this time carpeted in swirls of silver-grey. Keeping her eyes firmly fixed on that muscular back and those lean hips, she followed— losing count of the corners, the rows of identical doorways. Only a matter of minutes ago, the wry thought struck her, he'd been the pursuer, she the pursued. It took outstanding strength of will, power of personality, to reverse a situation so instantly and effortlessly as that. She'd met her match—in more ways than one. The prospect caused mingled alarm and excitement to pump adrenalin through her veins. In one way, she had waited for this moment all her life. In another, she had spent all her life evading it.

He glanced back just once, just to make sure she was still following him—not that he was in any doubt, she guessed. Catching her eye, he smiled. The softening of those stern features into that other, more approachable mould did nothing whatsoever to lessen her tension. It was all one, all part of the man. Stiffening her resolve, she tossed her auburn hair and hoisted her bag further up on her shoulder.

'Here we are, then.' Halting by one of the identical doors, he held it open for her to go through. She stood looking about her at another of those outer offices— this time a particularly spacious, airy one—lavishly equipped with every modern convenience. Not least among these was an attractive blonde secretary, whose lively blue eyes lit up under fluttering lashes as she registered Alex's arrival.

'Mr Grant! We weren't expecting a visit from you today, were we?' Her tone made it clear that the surprise was entirely pleasant. 'Have you been at this Special Meeting up at the Shrine?'

Alex treated her to his most engaging grin. 'Hallo, Jan. That's right; it's all over now, so we thought we'd escape down here.'

She nodded intelligently. 'How did it go?' Her gaze

moved sideways, detaching itself reluctantly from his face to rest on Josie's enquiringly.

'As expected,' he shrugged. 'As the scriptwriters intended.'

Josie pricked up her ears. At least there was an outpost of this great machine where one was permitted a hint of healthy disrespect. She caught Alex's eye.

'Sorry, Josie—this is Jan, who rules the roost here in the Planning Department. Jan, this is Miss Barnes—the archaeologist from Summerford,' he explained.

So that was where they were. The Planning section of Wallace Holdings—where, it figured, Alex would conduct most of his dealings with the huge firm.

Jan favoured Josie with a gleaming smile, which she grudgingly—and rather weakly—returned. 'I've heard all about you,' she remarked cryptically. Then she turned back to Alex. 'I'm afraid Mrs Platt and Mr Juniper aren't here. They should have been at the meeting—they haven't come back down yet.'

'Yes, they were there—conspicuous among the Other Ranks.' Alex didn't even bother to hide his dry disapproval of the whole scene. 'When I left they were all about to push off, doubtless to celebrate their victory with a wee dram in the MD's suite. Unless I'm sadly mistaken, they won't be down for at least an hour. That's why I've brought Miss Barnes—we need a quiet corner for a chat. We have . . .' he glanced in Josie's direction, 'one or two matters to sort out about the site.' His voice was light, charming. He turned his steady gaze back to Jan. 'I thought we might use Michael's office, since it's empty—if that's okay with you?'

Jan's beam was dazzling. 'You're welcome. Shall I bring you some tea?'

Josie was on the point of refusing stiffly: interruptions by this pretty fan of Alex Grant's would not, in her opinion, help an already difficult confrontation. But Alex had replied swiftly for them both before she could

get a word in. 'That would be wonderful, Jan. You're
an angel.'

The beam widened to display perfectly even, white
teeth. 'Not at all. It's a bit slack round here with
everyone away upstairs. Nice to have some company.'
She stood up, switching off her electric typewriter,
eyeing Josie now with open curiosity. 'So, you're the
archaeologist at Summerford?'

Josie opened her mouth to agree, but once again she
was pre-empted by Alex, who appeared to have decided
she was incapable of speaking for herself. 'No less than
the Director of the Dig,' he confirmed, a trace of
admiration underlying the irony.

'You won't have been too pleased about this recent
decision then?' Jan surmised.

'No.' This time Alex allowed her to answer for
herself: at least she had graduated to free speech, that
was something! 'I wasn't.'

Jan's expression now contained an element of
sympathy, much to Josie's surprise. 'It must have been
a bit of an ordeal, this meeting,' she observed. 'I expect
you could do with that tea.'

'Yes.' Josie barked out the ungracious monosyllable in
reply to both comments. She yearned to be back at the site
in the open air, among people and things she felt at home
with—not here in this overblown building and all it
represented. She longed to have the interview with Alex
over and done with. At the same time, she longed to find
herself alone with him again. All her instincts were
confused, it seemed; all her wires crossed. She must get in
touch with her violent, justified anger. That was the only
thing now that would see her through.

She turned, looking for Alex. He was halfway across
the room, striding towards another door; but Jan had
not finished with him yet. 'You'll be wanting to show
Miss Barnes Exhibit B1, Mr Grant,' she called after
him. Josie glanced at her; surely there was something
sly under her cheerful tone?

Alex stopped and flicked her a brief grin. 'I just might at that, Jan.' Then he opened the inner door, motioning to Josie to follow him in.

She went without a murmur. 'I'll be in with your tea,' Jan called as the door closed behind them.

Josie found herself confronting him alone, at last, in a small, sumptuous, soundproofed den. He sat himself carelessly on the edge of a huge new desk which dominated the room—on which, Josie noted with a secret stab of humour, reposed three pushbutton telephones in different colours. 'Sit down,' he ordered peremptorily.

Josie put down her bag, briefcase and jacket. 'Thanks, I'd prefer to stand.' She moved as far away from him as possible in the confined space, so that she was leaning up against a bright red filing cabinet.

'Just as you like.' Folding his arms, he perused her intently. Keen brown eyes locked with defensive green ones. She held his gaze for several seconds, then found herself once again studying her toecaps.

This was not like her; she was never the first to give way in any contest of wills. The strain of everything— the meeting, the last few days—must be beginning to tell. Drawing herself up, pulling in a long breath, she raised her eyes to his again. 'Alex . . .'

'Josie,' he began at precisely the same moment. Then, surprisingly, he chuckled. 'After you,' he invited with an exaggerated display of chivalry.

'No.' She was wrung out, irritable. 'Say what you've got to say. You've dragged me down here when all I want is to go home . . . you've marched into my life, barged into my caravan, mucked me about . . . what's it all about; what's the big deal? What,' she demanded, bracing herself for the big one, 'do you want from me, Alex?'

He did not answer at once, but continued to stare thoughtfully at her features as they worked through from weariness to infuriation to rage to genuine bewilderment. His earlier heavy irascibility had given way to a tautly-tempered control. 'Mucked you about? Is that what I've done?' he echoed softly, His eyes narrowed. 'I think it takes two to concoct a situation like we've got ourselves into, Josie,' he pointed out smoothly. 'If there's been any ... mucking about, I don't think I've been the only guilty party.' He paused. She stared away from him, into a corner of the room. She was not much good when it came to analysing interactions like theirs. She had always kept her emotional life simple—virtually nonexistent. She felt out of her depth, drowning in those shrewd dark eyes which never left her face.

'As to what I want from you,' he continued in a low voice, 'that's not easy to say, in a sentence or two. Maybe I want you. Maybe I like you. Maybe I find you a—challenge. Maybe,' he suggested carefully, 'I want to help you.'

This triggered off an explosion—as perhaps it was meant to. '*Help* me? That's a good one! With friends like you, Alex, I'd be in no need of enemies.' All at once she could bear this no longer, and she stooped, picked up her bags and jacket, and began to make for the door. 'I've had enough of this,' she muttered. 'I'm off.'

But he was there already, blocking her way. 'Oh no you don't,' he warned, and he meant it. 'You've escaped me once when I'd decided to put my position to you; you're not doing it again.' She retreated, sighing, put down her things again and regarded him warily. He came back to sit on the corner of the desk, a few feet from where she stood. 'Look, Josie.' He was direct, straightforward—in charge, but gentle. 'Things aren't easy between us, I know ... but can we ignore all that just for a few minutes? For God's sake let's try to consider this thing calmly, see where we both really stand. I'm here to tell you exactly what's been going on; and you're here, this time, to listen to me,' he added meaningfully.

She thrust her hands deep into the seam pockets of her skirt. 'Okay,' she conceded—accepting the inevitable but refusing to meet his eyes.

'When I came to Summerford on Sunday,' he began, with slow vehemence, 'I wasn't expecting to meet anyone like you. But whatever the Project Director was like, I certainly assumed she'd have been put fully in the picture. I never expected to be plunged into all this . . . lack of communication. That,' he asserted firmly, 'wasn't my fault, any more than it was yours. And it's no good complaining, because neither of us can do a thing about it. If Wallace Holdings chose not to enlighten you until the decision had been made a full week . . . well,' he shrugged, 'that's their business.'

'Business is right,' Josie had to interrupt. 'That's all they care about. Fascist manipulators. Unfeeling . . .'

'Don't waste your energy on empty insults,' he advised curtly. 'It won't do you any good, it doesn't impress me, and no one else is here to appreciate it. My own personal opinion may not, as it happens, be far removed from yours; but I have a duty to them, Josie. They may not be my bread and butter, but they're certainly responsible for providing the jam,' he added sardonically.

'You've said it.' She stared at him now, full in the eyes. 'That fat cheque—that's what it all boils down to, isn't it—at the end of the day, as your wonderful Chairman might say?'

He returned her stare for a full ten seconds before he remarked: 'I'd say it was more a question of maturity and professionalism than money. I'm well enough established in my trade without having to be concerned about that. And, Josie,' he pointed out quietly, 'he is not "my" chairman. I'm under contract to him for this scheme, that's all. I'm my own boss, beholden to no one. Don't you forget that. I choose whom I work for and what I do. No one else does.'

'Well then,' she retorted, 'I'm surprised you take on

work for people like this. Smug, self-important,
jumped-up little men, just like him. This place is
crawling with them. Ugh!'

Out of the blue, he dragged the conversation back to
the personal. 'What makes you so bitter, Josie?' he
asked softly. 'What grudge have you got against the
whole human race—and perhaps the male half of it in
particular?'

She flinched inwardly from this piece of sharp
insight. He was at it again—probing the inside of her
head, even her heart. 'I don't see what that has to do
with you—or with any of this,' she countered heatedly.
'Can we just stick to hard facts? Okay, so you arrived at
the site. Okay, so you thought I'd know too. Okay, so
you're getting a hefty whack for your plans of the
scheme, and you'll get more, and sooner, if the work
resumes sooner rather than later. So what? Did you
bring me in here to tell me that?'

'I've never known anyone so difficult to talk to,' he
complained, despairing. 'You're so touchy, you jump
to instant conclusions and land in all the wrong
places. You'd rather do anything—*anything*,' he
repeated with studied emphasis, 'than face a conflict
out. I'm trying to tell you, Josie, that I do have the
odd moral scruple. I'm interested in archaeology,
and—as it happens—I'm interested in you. I may be a
hard-headed businessman, but I'm a creative artist
too; and I'm a human being before I'm anything.
When I saw what you were actually doing, and what
it would mean if you had to abandon it halfway . . .
when I met you . . . I reached a firm decision of my
own. One way or another, I'd find a way round this
predicament. I can't back out of my own obligations
. . . but, as I said to you two nights ago, there are
usually compromises to be found if only people are
willing to look hard enough for them.'

'So what went wrong?' What was she supposed to
do—fall at his feet in gratitude? 'You haven't exactly

achieved anything with all this . . . compromising,' she reminded him.

'Not yet.' The echo of sincere disappointment in the phrase was mirrored in his eyes. 'But we're working on it, Vicky and me. Without sacrificing our own integrity we're looking into ways and means. We may be on the opposite side from you in one sense, Josie, but I've already told you—nothing's that cut and dried. Not in this or any other part of life.'

'Yes. You have already told me,' she shuddered, recalling the moment only too well. 'So, what are these . . . compromises?' She made the supreme effort to believe him, schooling her voice to a more rational pitch. 'Up against this lot, I should think it was like a fly kicking a football.'

His grin shot sparks straight through her. Whatever mood he presented, he had an uncanny knack of breaching all her defences. 'A bit like that. But flies can be very persistent. Remember David and Goliath.'

A tactful knock at the door heralded the appearance of Jan, preceded by a tray on which were two dainty cups, a bowl of sugar and a plate of petit beurre biscuits. Nothing but the best for the staff and guests of Wallace Holdings. 'Tea up!' she chanted sweetly.

Alex sprang from his perch to take the tray from her. 'Thanks, Jan. We need this, I can tell you. Negotiations,' he announced satirically, 'are proceeding slowly. It's thirsty work.' He grinned at Josie; but she only scowled. He need not think he could get round her that easily, like some featherbrained secretary.

'Thanks,' she growled, knowing she sounded prim and stilted. Then the aromatic steam rose to her nostrils, and she knew just how right he was. It was welcome.

'Not at all.' Jan cast an inquisitive glance from one to the other, as if testing the atmosphere. Then, with a quick—almost conspiratorial—smile at Alex, she made a dignified exit—every movement implying that she knew when three was a crowd.

'Nice girl.' Alex spooned sugar into his cup and stirred it.

Josie could think of no constructive reply, so she sipped her tea, allowing its restorative properties to percolate through her numbed mind and body. Her spirit returning, she put the cup down on the filing cabinet behind her and faced him with renewed vigour. 'Can we get to the point?' she demanded. 'Or was that it? So, you came to check out the site. So, it had nothing to do with whether I knew or not. You had no vested interest in keeping me in the dark. Wallace Holdings had not told you to come and soften me up. Then you saw our wonderful work, and made a snap decision to find a ... solution that might satisfy everyone. Even me.'

'There was nothing snap about it,' he corrected heavily. 'Vicky and I thought about it hard, and talked about it long into the night. But that's about the size and shape of it, yes.'

'So what do you want? A medal?'

'I simply want you to believe,' he replied instantly, deliberately, 'that we are trying. That there's common ground between you and me. If you'll accept that, in the context of the site—well, perhaps you can accept it in other contexts too.'

She glanced up at him sharply. Was he telling her he was still interested in her as a person—even after Wednesday night's fiasco? She tingled all over, and then she panicked and bristled. This sounded too risky by a long way. One of her defence systems might have been pulled away from under her feet—but there were others. There was still good old anger. She'd have to fall back on that—after all, there was plenty of it still seething inside her.

He had almost succeeded, with his smooth talk, in convincing her of his honourable intentions. Fool that she was, she had almost given way and taken him at his word. She reminded herself sternly of the way he had not even warned her what was about to happen—the way he had insinuated himself into her good books—the way he had so selfrighteously rejected her physical advances. Her own sense of shame and rage did the rest. Self-disgust mingled with self-defence is a potent force.

She lifted her head, thrusting out her small chin proudly. 'I don't believe you, Alex,' she said firmly. 'It all sounds great—but it doesn't hang together. I wasn't born yesterday. I haven't just fallen off the tree. I know the world, and it's dog eats dog, weakest to the wall, all that stuff. You're no different from all this lot here!' She waved a hand round the room in an expressive gesture. 'You're tarred with the same brush. There's no room for a human face in the big business scene—you know that as well as I do. It's just so much window dressing. All that garbage at the meeting, singing the praises of my project . . .'

'I have to tread a tight line,' he interrupted tersely. 'Can't you see that? I owe these people a clear statement of all the facts. *All* the facts, as I see them. My emotional sympathies may be with you, at least partly—but my professional credibility . . .'

'Damn your professional credibility!' The words were a match to dry tinder. She flared up, totally and once and for all. 'All you care about are your precious houses and your pay packet. It's all just empty words, hot air, and you know it. Just think what it does for the firm, too,' she taunted, well into her stride now, 'all that sensitive talk about the validity of our work. Such a show of human concern—the acceptable face of capitalism, no less!' It was a relief to be on safe ground. You knew where you were with anger. Unpleasant and uncomfortable it may be, but at least it was safe. It left no room for other, less desirable emotions to flood in. 'And who better to display it for the great firm,' she steamrollered on, 'than their tame architect? As long as you all make quite sure he hasn't a leg to stand on when the crunch comes. After all,' she sneered, 'you wouldn't want to risk your *professional credibility*!'

Her colour had risen along with her voice. Even the Titian of her hair seemed to deepen its rich fire. He stared down at her, his face creasing into lines of sheer exasperation. Then he shook his head sadly; his voice was low and controlled.

'Do you really mean all this, Josie? Is this really you, all this ranting and raving . . . or is it some furious perversion of your real self?'

Her stomach lurched. His reaction to her outburst was once again so unusual and so perceptive that it very nearly stopped her dead in her tracks. In her experience rage only bred more rage: temperamental eruptions set each other off like so many rockets. Meeting heat with cool analysis, or irrational prejudice with real feeling, were not what she was used to.

But she twisted his words in her mind until they merely added fuel to her flames. 'What do you mean—do I really mean it? There's no call to be patronising as well as dishonest!' She spat out the last word, instinctively aware that it would hurt him. 'How can you expect me to accept what you say? Have you forgotten what they—what *you*,' she stressed, 'have done to my potential allies—the Council and the Commission? Buying them off with bribery and corruption? Neat little promises of jobs for my team—*my* team,' she emphasised, working herself up into a lather, 'on a *building site*? Sloshing cement about—erecting *your* houses . . .'

Just for a moment, she ran out of suitably scathing, bitter phrases. Alex seized his opportunity, this slight crack in her wall of fury, and was off the desk and standing right in front of her in one stride. His brows had met in a heavy frown. His eyes, deeply troubled, penetrated hers. His voice was harsh, desperate as he ground out words to break through her torrent of abuse.

'For Christ's sake, Josie Barnes,' he grated, 'shut up. Just shut up. I don't want to hear another sound out of you. If there's only one way in the world to get through to you, woman,' his voice throbbed, dangerous now, 'then that's the way I'm going to have to take. If there's only one way to convince you I care . . . and to stop that beautiful mouth of yours . . . for two minutes at a time . . .'

At every second he was drawing closer, his hands coming up to frame her face—cool, smooth on her heated skin—fingertips subtly stroking her burning cheeks, thumbs tracing the outline of her angry, pouting lips. Involuntarily, they parted—at once a gesture of sensuality and consternation. Her eyes widened in horror, disbelief; her voice dried in her throat. She sensed the fury ebbing in her, a receding tide, and her features crumpled into submission.

When he bent to seek out her mouth with his, her whole body welcomed the invasion. Pliant curves strained against taut muscles. Her soft mouth opened to his fierce probing; the kiss seemed endless, engulfing. It was Alex who finally broke away, his hands leaving her face, sliding down over her neck and shoulders to hold her arms.

His eyes were glazed, and darker than ever. 'Josie!' Her name was an explosion; husky, impassioned. 'This is crazy. What are we doing to each other? I don't want to hurt you.'

She mustered all her resources—moving away from him, out of reach, out of temptation. 'You've got a funny way of showing it.' She backed away further, regarding him suspiciously.

He closed his eyes and shook his head hard, as if to clear his mind; then he turned his back on her and walked to the door. She picked up her bag, briefcase and jacket and—after a moment's hesitation—followed him. It seemed there was no more to be said. The interview was concluded—and inconclusive.

Jan looked up as they entered, smiling brightly. 'Wound up your discussions? Satisfactory, I hope?'

Josie did not trust herself to speak; but Alex was already in charge again. 'Fine thanks, Jan. Oh, and thanks for the lovely tea. I'm afraid we've left the tray.'

'That's all right. I'll have to tidy everything up soon—it'll be time to go home. I don't suppose they'll be back down now,' she went on cheerfully. 'Probably still carousing up there on the fifth floor. Okay for some, isn't it?' When they failed to answer, she peered closely at them for a second and then went on with her typing.

''Bye, then.' Alex was making for the door. 'Thanks again.'

'Not going to show Miss Barnes Exhibit B1, then?' Jan's fingers were still flying rapidly over the keys, but an odd little smile played on her face.

Alex halted, turned and looked at Josie. His expression was inscrutable: was there just the hint of a gleam in the dark eyes? 'Want to see it, Josie?'

Since she had not the remotest idea of what this famous exhibit might be, she could hardly refuse or accept. Perhaps she was a little curious. She shrugged slightly, raising her eybrows in a noncommittal gesture. 'If you want to show me.'

'I think perhaps I do,' he said pensively, his gaze never leaving her face. 'This way. Won't take a minute.'

Leaving Jan tapping merrily, he led Josie through yet another door to yet another inner sanctum—a larger one this time, full of shelf systems stacked with papers. Three out of four walls were covered with charts, plans and designs—and across the centre ran several long tables, on which stood perfectly constructed models of impressive building complexes.

He indicated one of these—the one at the end, the biggest and finest of all—with a triumphant flourish. 'Exhibit B1,' he announced proudly, his eyes flashing challenge.

Josie's first impulse was to run away from this new threat. She was in no doubt what the model represented; and she had a strong suspicion it might be better not to stay around and expose her already raw reactions to even worse irritants. Goodness knows where her hot temper might lead her this time.

But she had come too far to retreat with dignity now; so she walked steadily up to it and studied it carefully, taking in every minute detail: the tiny replicas of houses, all to scale, everything present and correct down to the last double-glazed window and solar panel; the miniature lawns and trees of the landscaped grounds; the small, stridently blue plastic swimming pool; even a few little human figures dotted about here and there to indicate relative proportions.

She could see it was a fine development; easy on the eye, streamlined without being brash—the best of modern design. It even looked comfortable: luxurious, she imagined, without ostentation—blending quite happily with its rural environment and the nearby village. Yes, she could picture it there all right—spreading across the fields at the Summerford site ...

The Summerford site. *Her* site. She glanced up at Alex, meeting the clear glint of irony in his eyes. Her blood surged—and finally came to boiling point. How dare he taunt her with this gratuitous, cruel barb? Just what did he think he was playing at—forcing her up here, cajoling her with smooth words, then attacking via her—baser instincts? Flaunting this symbol of his triumph—her defeat—right under her nose?

Pumping adrenalin lent force to her anger and power to her elbow. She simply reached out with both hands and pushed at the edge of the offending table with all her might. It leaned, teetered on two legs, poised for a split-second in mid-air—and toppled, landing on the thick pile of the carpet with a dulled crash. Alex had to jump out of the way as his own laborious handiwork smashed and splintered to a thousand pieces about his shoes.

She gazed at the ruins with a glimmer of satisfaction. Then she raised her eyes so that they locked directly with his. 'I hate you, Alex Grant,' Josie declared succinctly.

Swinging round on her heel, she left him there; she left the room, and the outer office, without a glance or a word to the astonished Jan. She walked along the corridor, summoned a lift; got into it, got out of it and marched across the lobby past the two flawlessly painted faces—who were just packing up to go home. Looking neither to left nor right, she crossed the courtyard to where her faithful little car waited for her—no longer squashed in between two obscenely over-polished Jaguars. She unlocked it, climbed into it and drove safely back to Summerford, suffused with a strange sense of elated calm.

This time, Alex made no attempt to come after her. She had every reason to suppose that would be the last she would see of him. And so what if it was?

CHAPTER SEVEN

WHEN at last she burst into the large caravan and flung herself wearily into the nearest chair, Simon was waiting for her, brandishing a wooden spoon over a bubbling pot which exuded pungent steam. He took one look at her unnaturally bright eyes and pinched expression, and went on with his laconic stirring.

'How did it go, then?' he ventured, when it became clear that she was not about to tender any information. 'You look a bit knackered,' he added helpfully.

'That's one word for it.'

He glanced up at her dry tone; then he tasted whatever he was concocting, frowning as he considered. 'Hmmm—more salt.' He found some among the litter on the table and threw a generous pinch into the pan. 'But what happened?' He was his usual laid-back self; unequivocal, as if it was all the same to him whether she told him or not. But Josie knew full well this was just a cover and in reality he was itching to hear every detail.

'Don't even ask.' She sighed, overcome now with utter exhaustion. That odd sense of exhilaration which had brought her home was wearing off.

His glance was sympathetic this time. 'Bad as that, was it?'

'Worse. Give me time to recover and I'll give you the whole sad story.' She sniffed the air like a hungry animal. 'What's that you're brewing?'

'Curry. Chicken and lentils. Okay?'

'Okay? How could it not be okay?' She smiled wanly at him. 'You're a friend in need, Si—and much better organised than me. Where did you find the time to cook, in among your day? I never do. For that matter, where did you find the chicken?' A shadow crossed her tense features. 'Did everything go all right, by the way? Any problems?'

'Thought you'd never ask.' He grinned mischievously, putting the lid on the pan and coming to sit opposite her. 'To take your queries in order of priority: everything here has gone like clockwork. You've got a fine team, Jo—brilliantly trained. It wasn't difficult at all to find a few moments to prepare a simple repast to greet the returning heroine.'

She grunted gloomily. 'The defeated, arriving in chains, more like. Still, I'm glad you all managed so well without me. Obviously I'm not as vital to the proceedings as I thought.'

Simon didn't miss the element of disappointment intermingled with her relief. 'No one,' he pointed out gently, 'is indispensable.'

She winced at this exact echo of Alex's phrase—was it really only this afternoon? It seemed that this was the week for putting Josie Barnes in her place; cutting her down to size. She changed the subject. 'So, what about this chicken? Did you go out shopping as well?'

'Oh no—the farmer's wife turned up with it just after you left. Your nice neighbour. She had several, apparently, and wondered if you could use one. So I took the executive decision on your behalf; and as I never refuse any offer, on principle . . .' he shrugged in the direction of the stove, 'there it is.'

The hard lines around Josie's mouth relaxed for a moment. 'That's Mrs Lawson all over. She's been sweet.'

'Well, at least you're not entirely alone against the world,' Simon observed, 'when I'm not around, that is. I find that reassuring, with all this going on.'

Yet again he was innocently repeating an earlier sentiment of Alex's. Yet again she flinched from the unwelcome memory. She had known that man less than a week; and already he had wormed his way into every level of her—continually springing to mind even when she was not anywhere near him in the flesh. No one had ever achieved such a thing before. She must take herself firmly in hand, at once.

After a meal which warmed her up in more ways than one (the first few forkfuls threatened to take the roof off her mouth, but with the aid of a glass of cold beer and a healthy appetite she soon got used to the spicy taste), Josie felt a lot better. Over cups of coffee, she regaled Simon with a blow-by-blow account of everything that had been said and done, from the moment she had arrived at the meeting to the moment she had left Wallace Holdings' premises.

Well, almost everything. If she left out one or two more intimate details, she could hardly blame herself for that. There were some exchanges one would not want even one's best friends to know about.

When she came to the part about overturning the model, she hesitated—and then went on. There was no reason why Simon should not hear about that too. He might find it quite amusing. She had nothing to be ashamed of—and her unpredictable temper was no stranger to him, after all. As she described it, she realised just how much she had relished that moment. A small smile of triumph hovered on her lips at the recollection.

He studied her for several seconds, one eyebrow slightly arched, and she had the strong impression he was sifting all the information through in his methodical way. But all he said was: 'Must have been a great feeling. Cathartic, I believe that's the word. Necessary release of built-up tension.'

'It was.' A little defensively, she went on, 'He had it coming, you know, Simon. After all that hypocritical stuff about trying to help me, and then having the nerve to think I'd want to see his wonderful creation . . . you should have seen his face when he took me in there—watching my every reaction—enjoying every moment.' Her throat constricted as she remembered her surging conflict of feelings just then.

Simon was never one to sit in judgment; but he had become thoughtful. 'Are you so sure he was being hypocritical, Jo? Isn't it possible he really is on your side—more than the others are, at least? You seem to have taken against this bloke in a big way.' His tone was almost offhand; but his eyes were alert. 'I know how accurate you often are at summing people up, but . . .'

'But what?' she snapped, much more loudly and quickly than she had intended.

He hunched his lanky shoulders. 'Well, you do seem to have made up your mind rather instantly about this—what's his name? Grant?—that he's a bad lot. Surely no one's quite that unscrupulous. I mean, his motives may be mixed—even if they're not as pure as the driven snow—there may be something you haven't understood.'

'So what are you suggesting? That my response is . . . irrational, in some way?' She struggled to banish the tremor of anger and anxiety from her voice. Maybe it hadn't been such a good idea to tell Simon everything, after all. He always had been a bit too perceptive for her liking. 'If you'd been there—heard them at it . . .'

'I'd have reacted just as you did,' he soothed her. 'I only wondered whether you'd given these architects a fair chance to show their true colours. At least they seem to be trying to find a way round it. That's more than can be said for any of the others.'

'Window dressing.' Josie drained the last of her coffee. 'A slick P.R. job, that's all it is. I wouldn't trust any of them further than I could throw them, and that includes Alexander Grant as much as the rest. Even Vicky Randle's in it with them—and I really rather liked her,' she mused regretfully—half to herself.

And you really liked him too, didn't you? Simon's quick mind supplied, with all the clear-eyed precision of an old and affectionate friend. But he knew Josie much too well to pursue that tack.

During the night spring showers turned to persistent rain, and all next day it poured relentlessly down, churning the field to a soggy mass. No keen villagers were going to come out in this looking for fresh air and exercise. Even the most ardent trainees were likely to stay at home today. So Josie and Simon took the opportunity to spend a few hours in the Portacabin going through the latest discoveries so that his expertise could be brought to bear on examining and classifying them.

Josie enjoyed nothing more than discussing her work with a fellow enthusiast. By the end of the afternoon she hardly knew where the time had gone. Her problems—both personal and professional—receded to a place near the back of her mind, almost out of the way; but never quite deserting her, niggling away at her memory like a thorn in the flesh. Over a cup of tea in the large caravan they summed up the day's labours.

'It's going really well,' Simon told her. 'You should be proud, Jo. Wait till it's all written up, do your career no end of good!'

'My career!' That was the least of her worries. 'If only I could finish the job! Just think what we could achieve, if we had the full year ahead . . .'

'You'll get a lot done in three months if you're organised,' he tried to cheer her up. 'If I take these samples back to the radiocarbon dating machine . . . no messing about—you'll have your answers straight away, down to the very year.'

But his words of comfort fell on stony ground. 'We could get even more done in another nine months,' she insisted morosely. 'It's so cruel!' she erupted, as the injustice of it all hit her yet again. 'The mean, arrogant . . .'

'Come on, Jo.' Simon picked up their cups and took them over to the sink. 'It's not like you to get so depressed. In fact I've never known anything get to you like this. I prescribe . . .' he thought for a moment, 'a nice quiet evening of mindless telly, some soup and sandwiches, a glass of wine. And a taboo on the subject of Wallace Holdings, or anything even remotely connected with it, for at least twelve hours. How does that grab you?'

She managed a sickly grin. 'Sounds like good advice.' But she knew it would never be far from her mind, even if she succeeded in keeping it out of her conversation.

By eight o'clock, as good as his word, he had them both seated comfortably in front of the small television set, plates of chicken sandwiches and mugs of tomato soup at their elbows. A quick rummage in his car had produced a bottle of red Spanish plonk, the effects of which were already beginning to dull Josie's emotional aches and pains just a little, superficially at least.

After taking a shower and changing into loose canvas jeans and a warm grey cable-knit sweater, Josie felt partly restored. Two sandwiches, several gulps of soup and two glasses of wine later, she felt almost content. The programme they were watching—an unbelievably inane quiz show—was rapidly reducing them both to a state of hysteria. Outside it was wet and raw; inside it was dry and cosy. Just for the moment, the rest of the complicated world could stay out there with the rain and take care of itself.

The TV screen was so small that Simon ended up sitting on the floor, propping his bony frame against Josie's armchair next to her knees, in order to see it properly. They polished off the soup and the sandwiches and embarked on their third glasses of wine, exchanging facetious remarks about the ridiculous antics of the contestants and doubling up with mirth at their own hilarious wit. It was always fun, being with Simon; thank goodness he was here now to share this tricky time . . .

'Pity Claire isn't here,' he observed laconically, and Josie realised just how much he must be missing his girlfriend.

'Sorry,' she muttered, strangely chastened at the thought.

'What for?' He turned round to look up at her.

'Well, you know—forgetting you must be—oh, I don't know . . .' She bit her lip. 'I'm so used to being alone, I sometimes forget other people need . . . each other . . .'

'Don't be a fool, Jo.' His grin was kind. 'You know what I meant.'

Her hand lay on his shoulder—a brief light touch. 'Of course. Just because I choose to be . . . independent, doesn't mean I don't understand how you feel.'

They sat for a minute without speaking; and Josie wondered secretly whether what she had just said was true. Did she really understand how it might feel, needing another person that way? Would she ever understand it? Did she even want to?

She sighed deeply. This was hardly the moment to try and work all that out, when her tired brain was far from lucid. She was not usually one for such complex philosophical thoughts: relationships, and all that— they usually left her cold. And tonight her body was pleasantly warm and relaxed; and out there a north-easterly was getting up, moaning spookily round the caravan so that she was extra glad not to be on her own.

What with the whine of the wind, the manic squawks of the quizmaster, the screeches of the studio audience, the drumming of rain on the metal roof—neither of them heard the sound of the vehicle throbbing to a halt not twenty yards away. Neither of them was aware of heavy boots striding across the boggy ground as an intruder made straight for the only light showing in the field—the powerful beam of his torch slicing ahead.

It was a matter of a moment for their visitor to leap the four steps, rap sharply on the door and thrust it open. Before Josie and Simon had time to react, let alone move, he was standing on the threshold, staring over at the intimate tableau they presented. His windblown hair seemed blacker than ever, glittering with raindrops which dripped over his upturned collar. Water ran down his cheeks and chin to glisten in his beard. Mud caked his boots and spattered the legs of his jeans.

A threatening, alarming invader, he reached behind him to slam the door shut, at once cutting out the fierce gusts which had entered the van with him. In that split second Josie was on her feet and Simon had swung round, surprise in every feature. But not before the dark gaze had swept over the comfortable huddle they made, with her hand on his shoulder, his head lolling near her knee—taken in the empty plates, bottle and glasses, the flickering screen, the atmosphere of relaxed familiarity.

'Alex!' Josie gasped out the single word, her wide eyes a translucent green as the glare of his flashlight caught them, the pupils shrinking to tiny, red-brown dots.

'I apologise. I'd no idea I'd be interrupting such a domestic scene.' The controlled irony in his voice was matched by a lifting of the damp dark brows. 'I was hoping for a few words with you, Josie, but I see I've chosen a bad moment.'

Simon had recovered his equanimity and was unfolding himself from the floor, running long fingers through his fair hair, his light eyes resting on the other man with calm interest. 'Not at all,' he assured him pleasantly. 'Come in. Have some coffee.'

Alex was studying Josie, whose gaze dropped before the harsh set of his jaw, the grim spark in his eyes. So, she was wrong: that was not the last she would see of him, this afternoon. He had come back for more. But more of what? More sparring and wrangling? Hadn't they done enough? Wasn't it time to call it a day? She raised her head defiantly to meet his accusing eyes. It was not for her to be daunted, after all. Surely he had asked for everything he got?

'Simon, this is Alexander Grant. Alex, my old friend and colleague Simon Raikes.'

Simon stepped towards Alex, holding out his right hand. 'Heard about you, Alex,' he said in his amiable, even tone.

Alex hesitated briefly; then, with a slight shrug, he took the offered hand and shook it firmly. 'Simon,' he returned coolly. 'Enjoying your visit?' he enquired in wry tones, his glance once again encompassing the cosy scene he had interrupted.

'Sure. I've come over from Cambridge,' Simon explained placidly, 'to make a closer inspection of Josie's bones.'

'Ah,' Alex allowed himself the hint of a grin in recognition of Simon's double-edged remark. *And a damn sight more than that*, his expression indicated clearly; but all he said was: 'How's it going?'

'Fine. We think they're pre-Christian,' Simon told him, waxing more eloquent than usual as he absorbed the potent electric charge running between his two companions, both of whom seemed curiously taciturn as they stared at each other. It seemed kinder to chatter on and cover their temporary lapse in communication. Now that he saw the two of them together, some of Josie's violent outbursts made better sense. Maintaining an inscrutable expression, he went blandly on. 'Some of the bits and pieces we've dug up with them are fascinating too. Amazing what our ancestors saw fit to send to the next world with their deceased . . .'

'I'm sure.' Alex's eyes were gimlets, drilling into Josie's. Then he tore them away and fixed them on Simon. 'I hate to break up the party, but I have something to say—in private. Mind if I steal her for a few minutes?'

'No party,' Simon assured him good-naturedly. 'Be my guest. Come back when you've finished your— business, have a cup of coffee.' He sprawled across a chair and picked up an archaeology magazine. Then he glanced up at Josie as a sudden thought appeared to strike him. 'Or would you rather I pushed off? I can always spend a bit of time next door, with the exhibits,' he offered helpfully, his grey eyes mild.

Josie pulled herself together. A conspiracy of males was all her life needed. She shot a scornful glance at Simon, but only received a blank smile in return. Gormless twit, she thought unkindly: can't he *see* I would rather not be left alone with Alex? Whose side does he think he's on, anyway? I thought he was supposed to be helping me?

Simon, who perhaps had his own ideas about how best he might help his old friend, was already buried in his magazine. Alex nodded in the direction of the door. 'No thanks,' he said briskly. 'Josie and I will go over to her caravan. Okay?'

He made it quite clear that it was an order rather than a suggestion. She glared at him, recoiling slightly as she encountered veiled hostility in his face. Then she shrugged, resigned. Whatever he had come to throw at her, she supposed she would have to take it. Obviously the previous afternoon's dramatic climax had upset him deeply. It might as well come now as any other time, the crunch; and she had a distinct feeling a crunch was what he had in mind, from the look on his countenance.

She picked up her coat, pulled on her boots and marched past him to push open the door without a backward glance at either man. By the time Alex caught up with her she was halfway across to her own caravan, head well down against buffeting wind and driving rain. She shivered, with chill and apprehension. This was no night to be exposed to unfriendly elements—inside or out.

He waited with exaggerated patience while she drew the curtains and lit the lamp and a small heater. Then she took off her coat and boots and sat demurely on one of the bunks, hands folded neatly in her lap, for all the world like a naughty child expecting punishment. Flinging off his jacket, he came to sit opposite her.

When he said nothing for several seconds, she drew a deep breath, raised her eyes and looked over at him

with an expression of deliberate, long-suffering weariness. 'What's it all about this time, Alex? Can't I even
have my Saturday night to myself now? I do have a life
to lead, you know.'

'So I gathered!' He was brusque, keeping himself on a
tighter rein than ever. She was obscurely pleased to note
that he disapproved of Simon's presence.

'Oh, you could have said what you had to say in
front of Simon. He's a close friend. We don't have any
secrets.'

'I dare say.' His voice was taut, his face hard.

'Just a friend,' she assured him lightly—in the kind of
tone that could, if you liked, imply the exact opposite.
Some gremlin encouraged her to let him think she and
Simon were more than that. Why should she disillusion
him, if he chose to misinterpret what he had seen?

'You could have fooled me. Anyway, Josie, I didn't
come here to discuss your personal life. Whatever
Simon is to you—or any other man is to you—that's
your affair.' He squared his shoulders.

'How true.' She smirked at his pun, whether
intentional or otherwise. 'So what did you come here
for? Haven't we done each other enough damage
already?'

A muscle twitched in his temple, as if he was
struggling to control his own anger—or some other
strong emotion; or perhaps a combination of several. 'I
came to say, Josie,' he replied—softly, carefully—'that
I'm sorry I subjected you to the indignity of seeing my
model of this development, just at that moment when
you'd had a difficult afternoon. It was a heartless thing
to do. I followed an instinct—some kind of intuition—
and now I wish I hadn't.'

'I'll bet you do,' she flung back, thinking of the mess
of cardboard and plywood all over the floor; the look
on his face, and then Jan's, as she had stormed out . . .

'Not for that reason. It wasn't as bad as it looked.
Jan helped me to patch it up.' Josie could imagine that

easily enough. 'No,' he went on, 'I'm sorry for how you must have felt when you saw it. Maybe I wanted to give you a jolt—shock you out of all that ridiculous anger—anyway, I'm here to apologise.'

Once again he was managing to undermine her defences with a totally unexpected, subtle attack. He seemed to know instinctively where her undefended points were. No one else had ever come anywhere near discovering them. It made her feel helpless and vulnerable, a snail stripped roughly of its shell—and yet, somewhere beneath the sense of exposure there was an odd kind of relief.

Confront her with equal measures of anger and hostility and she would match them, strength for strength. But deal in sensitive humanity—show even a hint of caring—and she was all but lost. Not that anyone often did—fortunately for her. Most men only seemed to know two ways of approaching a woman like Josie; and this was not one of them.

'I suppose,' she suggested stiffly, 'you expect me to apologise too, for overturning your fine work of art and insulting all it embodied?'

'No I don't.' Whether or not he thought she should, his tone implied, he knew full well she wasn't likely to.

'Well,' she admitted with extreme, rare caution, 'I regret any damage I may have caused. But,' she went on, climbing quickly on to safer ground, 'I don't for a moment regret doing it. It was one of the best things I ever did.'

'I should think it was a great moment,' he agreed gravely, refusing to rise to her bait again. There was even a spark of amusement in his eyes as he recalled it. Obviously, anger had not been his only reaction—not by a long way. Unless she was much mistaken, he was even allowing himself a touch of admiration.

It was time now to accept the olive branch he had come to extend, and offer one of her own. She had learned that much from him, at least; but—faced with the challenge—she knew she could not do it. There was still too much anger there; still a nagging, lurking deposit of it to be fought through. 'I still think you've played a despicable game with me, Alex,' she insisted, 'using me; keeping me dangling while Wallace Holdings pushed things along nicely their own way.' She was heating up satisfactorily now: that was better. 'I still think your talk of compromise was just a lot of—big words. Just buying time while the scheme went through. I don't believe you ever had any intention of . . .'

It was too much for him, this determination to keep up the self-imposed sense of injustice. At last she had broken through his thin veneer of restraint which was, tonight, dangerously fragile. Something in Alex snapped almost audibly, and a second later he had crossed the space to arrive beside her; once again she found that fingers like vices were encircling her upper arms.

'*You* talk to me about using?' he rasped. 'With your undeveloped notions of what feelings are—or any normal, human expression?' His Scottish accent became sharp as his own emotions rose to a peak. 'Why must you persist in seeing yourself as the victim of some evil male plot? Isn't it time you got your pretty head together and gave up fencing at the world like a spoilt child? I tell you this, lady—you're set on to auto-destruct!'

He was very close; and the male scents of him filled her nostrils as his barbed words rang round her head with a horrible truth. 'I'm no sex object, Josie,' he whispered harshly. 'Some kind of machine to release your inner tensions. But if this is the only way to breach your defences—well, maybe I'll have to use it after all. Maybe,' he added, and his tone was almost cruel, 'you're right: we should both take what's on offer and be grateful.'

She searched desperately for some clever, cutting retort; but sentences would not even form themselves in her head, let alone emerge. She froze in his tight grip, bombarded from outside by the whiplash of his words, from within by her own wanton, timeless, uncontrollable responses to his touch.

And suddenly, she knew she was not going to fight it. The truth of the matter hit her, fair and square, right in the solar plexus. She wanted him: *really* wanted him. She wanted this man in a way she had never wanted any man before in her life. She wanted his perceptive sympathy and his tough aggression and his burning creativity and his potent sexuality. For her, at that moment, they all rolled themselves up into one flame. They were there in every flicker from the dark eyes, every twist of the firm mouth, every gesture of the expressive hands. They were a heady brew, and she wanted them. And he, it appeared, wanted her.

It was all right, she reassured herself weakly before she finally went under his spell completely. It was all right for this to happen—because, after all, she still did not actually like him . . . only yesterday she had told him she hated him and meant every letter of it. It was not as if she had not wanted men before—though never, it had to be admitted, with this blistering urgency; but as long as she pulled the shutters down—made quite sure her emotions were securely locked away—it had been all right. Surely it would be all right this time too?

What was more, she would show him this was no way through her armour. He was wrong if he took her for one of those foolish impressionable females, to be won over by a few kisses and cuddles. She'd seen it all before; he had a shock coming if he thought . . .

Her last mental ramblings dispersed as his hands slid slowly up her shoulders and neck to seize her face—thumbs under her chin, bending her head back so that he could stare freely down into her eyes for long, intense moments. Then his seeking gaze moved to linger on the passionate pout of her lips—which parted under its pressure as if his mouth was already taking them . . .

and he was closing in, following up the promise with the action, his lips unerringly finding hers—cool, dry, firm on hers—brushing and insinuating, softly teasing.

No amount of force could have achieved such a devastating effect. Josie gasped; her eyes involuntarily closing, her body stiffening in every sinew. Then it relaxed and curved itself into his, yielding its softness to his hard planes. Her arms had wound themselves round his neck, fingers buried in the thick, damp, springing hair—pulling him down, urging him closer. Her mouth opened under his—inviting, demanding more intimate knowledge of his. Her body sprang into aching, pulsing life.

But Alex was taking his time—staying in charge. That message rang clear from the way his hands held her head away from his, breaking the kiss while he allowed his eyes to make another deliberate tour of her dazed features; the way the tip of his tongue merely tasted the sensitive inner skin of her lips, driving her into a frenzy of longing before it gradually—unhurriedly—deepened its explorations.

She felt impotent, frustrated—craving so much, yet unable to take it: and it was a shocking revelation. In her previous encounters with men, they had always been the desperate ones—grabbing at her, consuming her, while she relished the sense of power that gave her. She would remain detached, finally giving them what they so badly wanted—or some of it, at least. And sometimes, she even got quite a kick out of it herself.

This time it was utterly different. Without warning, her mind switched itself off and vanished; her oldest, staunchest ally deserted her, leaving her the willing victim of waves of pure passion. She was barely aware of what was hitting her: just that the waves were washing over her, dragging her deeper into swirling, deliciously dangerous waters—pulling her under, murmuring in her ear that the current was even stronger, the water even warmer the further into it she went . . .

When his mouth left hers to trail gently across her cheek, the wiry hairs of his beard and moustache leaving a tingling path of their own, she moved her head impatiently, her lips seeking his again—drugged, unsatisfied. This time she gave her hands free range of the strong outlines of his body—running themselves up and down the long back, feeling the muscles in his arms, the power in his shoulders, through the smooth weave of his brushed cotton shirt.

And this time he let himself go—plundering her mouth, allowing his own hands to wander and stroke and feel and explore as they liked; and she did not stop them but willed them on, her skin sparking electricity wherever they touched it, her insides aching with the desire to know him—all of him—as he possessed her.

And that was the only possible way ahead, of course. Where else would they find themselves but stretched horizontal on the narrow bed, welded together, burrowing frantically through layers of obstructive clothing—in the one, overpowering urge to reach one another—to get as close as two people can possibly be? There was nothing in the world, then, but his subtle fingertips on her taut breasts; and then his tongue and sensitive lips taking over as those confident, busy hands slid lower—releasing buttons, parting a zip, stroking the soft white flesh of her waist and stomach—slowly, very deliberately extending their captured territory down her hips and abdomen, round her thighs, until she caught her breath and clasped him tighter, knowing only that she would explode with the new surge of need he had tapped in her.

The only sounds in the tiny cabin were their heavy breathing; and from outside the thunder of rain on the roof, the howl of wind—which kept up its running commentary, occasionally shaking the whole caravan as if to startle them back to reality. But it would have taken more than a passing gale—nothing short of fire, flood, earthquake, holocaust—to deter Josie from her

chosen course at that moment. All her defensive rage
had been obliterated, buried under a landslide of sheer
sensuality. Instead of being her worst enemy, Alex
Grant had become her immediate destiny—her one and
only conscious goal.

But she had reckoned without the man himself, or the
outstanding force of his will. When other men might
have passed a point of no return, Alex drew back. Just
as she expected a total merging, a mutual release—he
withdrew; he left her, alone and vulnerable, staring up
at him through huge, dilated, passion-clouded green
eyes. Standing up, he tucked his shirt into his jeans,
buckled his belt, did up a few buttons. His gaze steady
on her face, he raked long fingers through his
dishevelled hair.

'Alex!' Huskily she appealed to him, arms unconsciously outstretched. 'What—what's the matter?'

His smile, incredibly, was warm and tender. It was
also calm and poised. 'Why?'

'But—I thought...' she stuttered—torn apart,
plunged into an abyss of loss, a cold nakedness she had
never dreamed of in her worst nightmares. 'I mean, you
don't have to ... you needn't ... we can ...' This was
appalling, terrible—even worse than the last time! What
did she have to say to make him realise how much she
wanted him? To tell him he did not have to stop there?
'I'm on the pill, Alex!' she declared, desperation lending
her a spurious boldness which she did not really feel.

He laughed—low in his throat, without real humour.
Then he sat beside her and took her hand. Reawakened
tremors shot through her, convulsing her body. How
she wanted him! She had never imagined it could be like
this, wanting someone ...

'I'm sure you are, Josie,' he acknowledged mildly.

'So ... ?' She struggled now to sit up, to cover some
parts of her exposed self, both physical and emotional.
Too late, too late! her mind ranted, creeping back from
wherever it had been hiding itself.

'So—How often do I have to say it? I'm not in the habit of making use of any other person. It's not my way. For me, all this has to mean something. And I'm not here to live out a lie—or to force a situation where you would be doing that.'

She could only stare at him in speechless disbelief. Talk about turning the tables—nothing in her life had prepared her for this! Last time, when she had deliberately used their mutual attraction as an escape route from further confrontation and he had politely refused her—that had been bad enough. But now—now, when she had allowed herself to go right under, to give way to something dangerously like real feeling for the first time ever—he was apparently rejecting her again. And, what was worse, it was obviously planned: he had known all along he was going to do it. It was a calculated, cold-blooded exposure. And she had fallen right into it.

His glance was kind on her incredulous face. 'You've made it clear that your feelings for me are negative, to say the least. Not much of a basis for all this, surely? Surely,' he pressed, more urgently, 'even you'd agree to that?'

She twisted her head away in an agony of embarrassment. 'I—I don't know.'

'I don't deny I'm attracted to you, Josie—very attracted. You're a lovely woman, and a lovely person. Anger and attraction are close cousins, though, when it comes to men and women. Physical compatibility just isn't enough, on its own.'

She shook her head dumbly. She had no weapons to counter such a profound level of attack. 'My sexual appetite,' he went on—still in that low, steady voice, 'is as normal as the next man's.' She did not doubt that—not for a second. 'Oh, I've been through all that sordid business of having to prove it in strings of meaningless conquests—to satisfy some obscure drive, or maybe it's male pride, I don't know . . .' His thumb was caressing her hand now, creating disturbances right through her body which he could not have guessed at. 'But I grew out of all that. That isn't what life's all about. If you don't care, really care about the person . . .' his tone hardened, 'it's not worth the hassle.' His hand came up to trace the delicate outlines of her face, featherlight fingertips running across her cheek, chin, the curve of her mouth.

She licked her dry lips, found her voice. 'But why—why did you. . . ?'

'Why let things get this far between us? It seemed the only way to break through to any real level of you, Josie. There's plenty going on between us—sexual tension, call it what you like. If that bubble has to burst before we can settle down to some kind of mature relationship, like two adults—instead of two perpetually scrapping adolescents . . .' he smiled slightly, 'well, as I said to you before, there's nearly always a solution, if you can be bothered to find it; and I decided this was the only way. Look at us now,' he pointed out, suddenly humorous. 'We're almost communicating! If you don't watch your step, Josie, we'll soon be having a calm, serious, personal conversation!'

She failed to share his gentle amusement. 'You mean,' she corrected sulkily, 'I'm not ranting at you.'

He shrugged. 'Whatever I mean, it's put a stop to your interminable gabbling of pointless hostilities. Venting all that fury at me—most of which, I suspect, had little or nothing to do with me. I may be its catalyst, but I'm not its cause. Perhaps one day,' he suggested very quietly, 'you might feel like telling me what was.'

She turned away, hiding as best she could the stabs of pain and embarrassment which were shooting through her. Gradually, the full implications of his words—of this whole situation—seeped into her brain; but there was no anger any more, only cold, stark shock. 'So . . . you decided to use . . . sex, to get back at me . . . instead of being angry . . .' Still avoiding his eyes, she muttered the disjointed phrases, sullen.

'Not back at you, Josie,' he denied instantly, vehemently. 'Through to you.' He took her hand in his again. 'And it worked, didn't it?' She made no reply, and he repeated, pushing her, 'didn't it?'

But she scrambled to her feet then—tidying her clothes, arranging her hair—anything to keep moving and escape answering him. She suspected there should be some kind of outrage in her somewhere; but the indignation was all gone. Nothing was left but a deep, raw hurt. She recognised it, even in her stunned state, as the suffering which has to be undergone before we can begin to understand ourselves. Something had shifted inside her. If there was any bitterness left, she knew it was no longer directed at Alex—but at herself.

He had stood up too and was reaching for his coat and boots. The decisive action shocked her, and she stared at him, bright spots of colour in both cheeks. How could he calmly walk out, as if they had shared nothing more than a routine social chat?

Reading her expression like an open book, he smiled again. 'Best if I leave you,' he said firmly. 'You'll be quite all right. You won't be alone, after all. Get straight back over to your friend Simon—carry on with whatever you were up to when I barged in . . .'

'We weren't—up to anything,' she growled. 'I told you, he's . . .'

'Whatever he is, it's none of my business,' Alex interrupted curtly.

'But I want to tell you—he really is an old friend, nothing more—he lives with someone . . .' Suddenly it was important—vital—that Alex should not get the wrong idea about her and Simon. Or her and anyone.

He thrust his hands into his pockets and studied her for a few moments, dark brows drawn together. 'Okay, Josie. You haven't given my word much credibility—but I'll take yours. I've got no reason not to believe you.'

She felt even more ashamed, and dropped her gaze to her feet. Yet another way in which she could learn from him. Now that it had started, would there be no end?

He stepped towards her and laid firm hands on her shoulders—renewing those recent responses which still pulsed so near the surface. Gazing intently down into her eyes—forcing them to come up and meet his, through the sheer strength of his will—he spoke to her as earnestly as she had ever heard him. 'Now, once and for all, Josie, I'm going to ask *you* to believe in one or two things. If you can't—well, then there's no future for us. If you can, you and me could be just beginning.'

He waited for a second, as if to give her the chance to make her usual cynical protestation. None came, so he went on. 'I have *not* had it in for you all along. I'm *not* the front man in some wicked universal plot to trap Josephine Barnes and force the path of her life to run crooked. I'm *not* Wallace Holdings' stooge, nor their dirty worker. I'm *not* a faceless, nameless example of my sex.'

His tone gathered warmth and emphasis. 'I'm an individual; a man. Alex Grant, architect—who genuinely wants to get to know you, Josie Barnes, a whole lot better. Who also hopes, quite sincerely, to help you through some problems you're currently bogged down in. All kinds of problems,' he commented cryptically. 'I haven't finished yet, on either count, not by a long way. Don't give up on me, Josie. Think it all through. And when you feel ready to face it out—discuss further possibilities . . . well, you know where I work. Give me a ring. Get in touch. I'll be there, waiting, never mind how long it takes.'

On this impassioned, slightly hoarse note, he dropped his hands from her shoulders and swung round—in the same positive, conclusive movement. Then he strode to the door, opened it, closed it—and was gone.

Alone, she listened to the sound of his steps as they merged with the restless whinings and whisperings of the wind.

CHAPTER EIGHT

THE next three days were a limbo: a patch of time that was out of time, and yet a crucial turning point in Josie's life. All her training and experience had to take over so that she could function on fully-automatic; meanwhile she did what she should have done years ago—what Alex had forced her to do: she opened her mind and heart, allowing deep, untapped thoughts and feelings to churn and process through—on and on, over and over until she was mentally and emotionally exhausted.

Instinctively he had spotted the truth about her. She was still a child, where it mattered. Not spoilt, perhaps; but certainly arrested at a critical moment of early development—that stage when the starkly simple emotional patterns of childhood must begin to give way to the more complex demands and offerings of adulthood. No one had taught her, by example or any other way; no one had given her the support every young person needs in order to achieve this transition.

Now, so many years on, Alex had taken it upon himself—acting on faith and instinct—to awaken her passionate nature which had become replaced by a hollow mockery of itself; to startle real feelings out of their deep hiding places; to show her that she had been feeding off just one genuine emotion all this time, and a negative one at that: anger and resentment.

And, like all bombshells, the explosion had been total, instant, devastating. Ten days ago, everything had seemed so simple: old traumas long since buried, Josie had learned how to cope with maturity by shutting all feelings out, never giving or exposing her real self. Then, before she knew what had hit her, that whole flimsy façade had all gone for a burton: her blindness to other people's real needs, her exaggerated ideals of pride and independence. Single-handed, this unusual, perceptive man had prised open her mind and heart to a painful truth: she had been a prisoner in a locked cage made of theories and superficial sensations. It was time to lower the drawbridge and let the feelings rush in to join them—and then, suddenly, they would begin to make sense. He had forced her to see, from the benefit of his own wisdom and experience—and, perhaps, from his own interest in her?—that heads and hearts do not occupy different worlds, but belong together—a unified strength, twice as valid. He had pierced through layers which no one else had ever tried to penetrate—creating major upheavals in the process so that her internal landscape could never be anywhere near the same shape again—whatever happened.

Now she lay awake through the dark lonely hours, giving way to rare, refreshing tears of shame, regret, understanding. *Don't despise yourself*, he had advised, in his sensitive way; but how could she help it, as she recalled the times she had drifted so coolly into some passing relationship or other . . . got what there was to be had out of it . . . drifted on again to the next shallow thing? Once in a while, when the man concerned had seemed to want the same from her, it had worked well enough on a totally superficial level—and, it had to be faced, plenty of men did. But far more often, now that she made herself look into them, those incidents had been potential disaster areas. She shuddered to think how close she must have been to inflicting—or even suffering—serious lasting emotional damage.

Well, all that was over now—shattered, blown apart by the events of the past week or so. She could face that knowledge: she was strong enough to learn from it and move on. But where did that leave her and Alex? So, he'd taken her by the shoulders and shaken her into a new depth of self-awareness—but where did they go from there? In the dead of night she schooled herself to face the final, million-dollar question: how did she feel about him?

At long last brutally honest with herself, she confronted a series of hard facts. She wanted him intensely, she liked and admired him enormously. That combination—lethal, she'd always called it—would have been enough to send her running, in the past; in fact it very nearly had this time. Being in his company was as easy and natural, and yet as stimulating and exciting, as anything she had known. It felt unreal to contemplate a past which had never included him. It felt desolate to envisage a future which would not contain him. Awareness of his presence and existence filled her every waking moment, and quite a few sleeping ones as well. She went about like a zombie. Her normal healthy appetite had deserted her. Simon was casting her wry looks and grinning to himself. Even the trainees whispered and giggled behind her back, or stared in undisguised curiosity when her concentration lapsed.

The signs pointed in just one direction: she was in love with Alex Grant.

But then, what were his feelings for her? This riddle had her baffled. Sexually and intellectually she might be far from green; but emotionally she was just starting out. How did you tell whether a man loved you? Or was really interested in you?

That electricity was there between them all right: what had he called it—sexual tension? But that, as she now knew, was only one part of a necessary whole. Was that all there was in it, for him? He had no time for empty sexual games, meaningless charades of the kind she had indulged in, she knew that. But perhaps, in desperation, he had decided to use their mutual physical need as a means to an end: the only way to reach Josie, to bring her to heel. Perhaps his own feelings had played no part at all in the policy decision. He had been using her, as she had used people in the past . . .

And so it went on, round and round, until she thought she was going mad. By Tuesday night she knew she would have to do something—and soon. Get in touch, he had said, give him a ring. In other words it was up to her to take the responsibility for the next step. When she was ready, he had said; when she had thought it through. The ball was in her court.

Of course, he might have meant nothing more than the next stage in any plan of action about Wallace Holdings. But she had a distinct suspicion he had meant much more than that. The importance of that other matter had dwindled to a pathetic storm in a teacup next to—all the rest. If she screwed up her courage and rang him now, he would understand that she realised that—and a whole lot else besides. Had she the strength to do it? Could she afford *not* to?

She wandered into the Portacabin at least five times during the course of Wednesday morning and stood staring at the telephone as if she was expecting it to come up with a solution. Then she turned round and went out again. Twice, members of her team came in while she was engaged in her private contemplation of it. Raising expressive eyebrows, but making no comment, they went about their business.

Just before lunch, when everyone else was in the caravan—washing their muddy hands, brewing up tea, tearing into packs of sandwiches—she paid yet another visit to the cabin, preferring her own company to theirs. This time she presented her back to the telephone, ostentatiously ignoring it while she attended to some dull, long-overdue paperwork. When its bell shrilled out just behind her she nearly leapt out of her skin. Her mind had been so occupied with whether or not she should pick up the receiver and dial Alex's number, she had all but forgotten that telegraphic communication works both ways.

'Summerford Project,' she told the mouthpiece, holding it in her left hand so that she could continue form-filling with her right.

'Miss Josephine Barnes?' The voice was female; brisk, efficient, organising. Josie was sure she'd never heard it before.

'Yes?' Puzzled, she put down her pen.

'Phyllis Ryder-Davies. Assistant to the Co-ordinator for Training Schemes. Cotswold Area.' The line positively reverberated with succinct information.

For a moment, however, Josie was none the wiser. Then she worked it out. 'Oh, you mean the *Commission*?'

'Precisely.' Miss, Mrs or Ms Ryder-Davies came straight to the point. 'About this Wallace Holdings business.'

'Oh yes?' The Josie of a week ago might have launched into an instant tirade, spelling out just what she thought of the Commission, caving feebly in at the first dangling of a tempting bait under their noses. Traineeships for all on the building site, indeed! But today she held her peace and kept her own counsel, giving them a chance to speak for themselves first.

'Yes. First—well done!'

'Pardon?' Josie closed her eyes. Was it just her, or was *every*one going mad?

'Well done. Latest news. Good show. How did you manage it?'

'Manage what?' Picking up her pen, she started doodling stick-figures on the official form she had been filling in. 'I'm sorry, Miss—er . . . I don't . . .'

'Ryder-Davies. Mrs. You don't mean to tell me you haven't heard? Good heavens! I'd have thought you'd be the first to know. They phoned us about it yesterday. I suppose they'll have written to you formally. Knowing the post these days, you'll be lucky if it arrives tomorrow. Really, when you think of the cost of postage, it's perfectly atrocious.'

Josie was rapidly becoming bemused. 'Look, Mrs—
er—Ryder-Davies, I really don't have any idea what
you're talking about. Last thing I knew, the news was
far from good. After the Special Meeting—which I
attended,' she added meaningfully, 'it looked like the
worst kind of news. Has something else happened?' She
made a valiant effort not to expect anything too good—
but optimism was stirring itself at the back of her
mind.

The lady chuckled fruitily. 'I should say it has. Nice
to be a harbinger of glad tidings for a change, in these
days of cutbacks and belt-tightenings. I nearly always
get the job of breaking the bad news.' Josie's knuckles
whitened as she gripped the receiver in her impatience;
but she said nothing. 'They've changed their minds,'
Mrs Ryder-Davies went on. 'Got round the problem
somehow. Seems someone hit upon a miracle solution—
some kind of compromise—we rather assumed it had
something to do with you. Especially since we couldn't
. . . get to the Meeting.'

Josie's excitement was rising with every word she
heard. Perhaps, after all, the fate of her dig did matter
to her, quite a lot. Keeping a careful rein on her voice,
she tried to get some more sense out of the
Commission's spokesperson. 'But don't you have any
idea what this compromise might be?'

'Sorry dear—no details. Expect it'll all be in your
letter. Main thing is, you and your team can go on
digging to your heart's content—till the year's up,
anyway. You don't have to pack up your buckets and
spades as soon as you thought. Might even have longer
than that,' she added obscurely. 'Something to do with
the construction people.'

'The builders?' Exasperation tempered her natural
delight. Meanwhile the pen—entirely of its own
accord—had taken to embellishing a handy telephone
directory with the initials *A.G.* in various tasteful
scripts. 'How do you mean?'

'As I say, Miss Barnes, I have not been enlightened as to the whole story. But it seems to be to do with the contractors being persuaded to make a start on another part of the development site. Not yours, you see,' she explained vaguely.

'You mean one of the other fields?' Josie knew there were several fields due to be covered by the development, not only hers; but surely it was not possible to dig footings and lay foundations in some places and not in others?

'That must be it.' Mrs Ryder-Davies was clearly not well-versed in the technicalities. 'Anyway, whatever's behind it, ours not to reason why, eh? Ours just to accept the reversal of policy and be grateful.'

'Well, yes, of course—but . . .'

'And if it wasn't down to you,' the other woman mused, her hearty tones effortlessly drowning Josie's hesitant ones, 'I'd give a lot to know whom we do have to thank.'

Josie had her own ideas about that one, but she refrained from venturing them aloud. 'Of course I'm delighted,' she said, 'and thank you for telling me— even if you did think I'd already know. I shall go back to planning my full schedule at once.'

'And you can tell that industrious team of yours they won't all have to leave you and start loading cement mixers,' Mrs Ryder-Davies pointed out cheerfully. 'Won't they be pleased?'

No thanks to you, Josie's mind intoned sarcastically; but she was far too happy and relieved to say it. 'Actually, I never told them. They'll never need to know how near they came to being transferred . . .' Thank God she had not given way to her depression and confided in them. She put the pen down, running a trembling hand over her auburn curls as the full implication of this news seeped gradually through her brain.

'Which brings me quite neatly,' the good lady was

saying now, 'to my other reason for phoning. We were considering it before all this happened, but it had to be shelved, of course, when the bad news broke. Now we can bring it up.'

Josie's pen was now experimentally scrawling *Mrs Josie Grant* all over a notepad which lay on the table. Frowning at herself in horror, she scrubbed out the tell-tale words till they were illegible, tore the top sheet off the pad, crumpled it into a tiny ball and threw it into the wastebin. 'Bring what up, Mrs Ryder-Davies?' she enquired with unusual tolerance.

'The Commission would like to offer you a permanent post, here in this area, after the Summerford Project is completed.'

'A *what*?' As reactions go, she knew it was ungracious and undignified; but she couldn't prevent it.

'A post,' elaborated Phyllis Ryder-Davies patiently. 'A position. A job.'

'What sort of job?' This was all getting too much; Josie leaned back in her chair, pressing her left hand to her throbbing head. 'I'm an archaeologist, you know, not a . . .' Not some kind of a petty bureaucrat, she was going to say, but she bit the words back just in time.

'Of course you are, my dear,' the lady reassured her soothingly, 'and an excellent one. And so good with the young people. That's just the point: we have so many interesting little projects, like yours, cropping up. Our part of the country appears to be quite loaded with fascinating—er—relics. We have new ones coming to light all the time.' She sounded so proud, you could almost imagine she was personally responsible for their presence.

'But where do I come in?' Using all her restraint, Josie succeeded in sounding intrigued but businesslike.

'I'm coming to that. The various local Councils feel that all such sites should be fully excavated, and we agree with them. Furthermore, they make ideal training schemes for the young unemployed—as you have proved. Since we're in the fortunate position of having funds at our disposal—not vast sums, you understand, but enough—we've got together and decided to appoint one or two full-time supervisors. To take overall charge, you see—make sure the teams are getting it right. Working from our offices, bur frequently visiting all the sites in the area.'

She paused in her flow just for a moment, and Josie thought she was supposed to make an intelligent remark; but before she had a chance to open her mouth, Mrs Ryder-Davies was off again. 'Now, since you've done such wonders with those . . .' she searched briefly for an appropriate word, 'youths at Summerford, and found such wonderful things, we think you'd be the obvious candidate. Naturally, we realise you have work in Cambridge to complete,' she bustled on, without giving Josie the opportunity to get a word in. 'But perhaps after you've tidied up the ends there . . . we understand your research fellowship is virtually at an end . . .'

At last she came to a natural break. If she could have seen the expression on Josie's face, she would have saved herself the trouble of sounding so persuasive. There would be important issues to think through, of course; such a major decision must be taken coolly, after careful consideration of all the plus and minus points. One didn't just rush into a thing like this, however strongly one's instincts pulled that way. She would have to go back to Cambridge, talk to colleagues, discuss it with Simon . . .

Good thing no one else was present to see the grin that was splitting her cheeks. 'I'll do it, Mrs Ryder-Davies,' she said.

The brief silence was louder than any words. Even this redoubtable lady was apparently unused to quite such instantaneous executive decisions. But she soon recovered herself. 'Splendid! Well done again, Miss Barnes! Nothing like a positive, firm approach! The Co-ordinator will be thrilled. Meanwhile, of course, we will get it down on paper—send you an official invitation—and perhaps, my dear,' she added kindly, 'you should take just a *little* time to think it over? Make sure you still feel so sure after you've taken all the pros and cons into account?'

'Don't worry,' Josie promised meekly, 'I will. And thank you.'

'Not at all. It's been going so well—we're only too glad it's going to be able to continue after all. Doubtless we shall all find out, in the fullness of time, exactly what made the great company change its corporate mind. The main thing is, they did. So—on with the good work!' she exclaimed in jovial tones. 'Back to your trowel!'

'On with the good work,' echoed Josie quietly. 'Goodbye, and thanks again.'

'Goodbye, Miss Barnes—for now,' barked Phyllis Ryder-Davies, harbinger of glad tidings.

After five minutes—some of which she spent staring blankly into space, the rest Tippex-ing out the scribbles she had made on the highly important form—Josie ran across to the large caravan and extricated Simon from among the noisy lunchtime scene.

'Sorry to interrupt such animated conversation,' she said as they strolled together round the peaceful field. 'I've got to have a private word.'

Simon took a bite of sausage roll, and flicked her a keen glance. 'You look really wound up—you're all pink. What happened to all that poetic chalk-white? Premium Bond come up? Won the pools?'

Josie danced several steps ahead of him. Then she recalled her impending new position of authority, and adopted a more sober, mature bearing. 'Much better than that. I've just had a phone call.'

'Oh yes?'

She turned even pinker, catching his wry expression. 'Not who you think,' she mumbled, momentarily shaken out of her euphoria. Then she grinned. 'From the Commission.'

'All of it?' He licked the last remaining crumbs from his fingers.

'Simon, this is serious. You've got to listen carefully.'

'I'm all ears—and deadly earnest. Just be gentle with me, that's all,' he grumbled. 'I've had enough bad news recently to last a year.'

'It's not at all bad. It's great. The best we could've had,' she bubbled. Then she told him—all of it.

At the end, he emitted a long low whistle. Then he snaked a skinny arm round her shoulders and gave them a quick squeeze. From Simon, that was the height of demonstrative exuberance. 'Wow! That's more like it! Clever old Josie! So—you'll be looking for a more permanent residence in these parts?'

'That's the general idea,' she agreed happily. 'After the Project's finished, of course. I might as well stay on here for the moment.'

He was eyeing her shrewdly. 'We'll miss you in Cambridge you know, Jo.'

She took his arm. 'Maybe, a bit. And I'll miss you all—a bit. But let's face it, Si—I've got no real roots there—never have had. Not there, or anywhere. I've always been an unattached sort of person. Maybe this is my chance to settle down in one place. I like it here, anyway,' she added, after a short pause.

'I rather gathered that.' He loped beside her, hands in pockets. 'Well, Claire and I can come and visit you. And you can come back and stay with us.'

'I'd like that—thanks.' It all seemed so real, as if it was happening already.

'Great news about the dig,' Simon was saying. 'You really don't know how they've wangled it?'

'I couldn't get a lot of sense out of this lady. Something to do with starting on a different bit of the development. I expect I'll find out soon enough.'

'I expect you will.' He whistled again, through his

teeth this time. 'Josie, I'll have to be getting back myself pretty soon. I'm glad this has happened because I wasn't happy about telling you, the way you were feeling. Now I'll feel a bit better about leaving you on your own. I must get this material back to be collated and dated, and then there are my students . . .'

'And Claire,' she finished for him.

'Well, yes.' He kicked at a stone. 'She phoned last night. I'd like to get back, really.'

'Of course you would,' Josie said warmly. 'I'm sorry—I've been so wrapped up in my own problems, I almost forgot it's been nearly a week.'

'That's okay. I thought if I pushed off on Friday—if you don't mind?'

'Mind? Simon, you've been wonderful—I can't tell you how helpful it's been, having you here just now. Of course you've got to get back.' She thought for a few seconds, and then went on: 'Can I ask you one final favour?'

'Sure. Even unto half my kingdom.'

She giggled. 'That won't be necessary. But I would appreciate some of tomorrow off. Would you mind being left in charge again? I've got—urgent business to sort out, in Bath, and I'd rather not do it on the phone. If you're here to supervise the mob, I can play truant long enough to . . . deal with it properly.'

'Excellent idea.' His glance was affectionate, concerned. 'You could do with a break, Jo. You'd better be going somewhere nice. If you're not planning something nice,' he admonished sternly, 'I won't stay and trainee-sit.'

'I don't know if you'd call it nice, exactly.' She was solemn now—pensive. 'In fact I expect it to be distinctly difficult. But it's something I've got to do—I *want* to do—and as soon as possible.'

'Someone you've got to see?' he enquired blandly.

'Could be.'

'Keep my big nose out, is that it?' He grinned. 'Sorry, Jo.'

'Don't be a fool.' She gave him a playful nudge in the ribs. 'I just don't want to talk about it—yet, that's all. Perhaps one day . . .'

They turned back again towards the caravans. Trainees were spilling out now in all directions, eager to get on with their activities. 'Well,' Simon said gently, 'as long as you're sure you know where you're at.'

'Don't worry.' There was a glow in her eyes which he had never seen before. Her voice was serene but confident. 'I've never been more certain.'

CHAPTER NINE

COMING to a major decision can be like shedding a great weight. That night Josie slept right through, waking refreshed and alert to greet a newly-washed spring morning. She hummed as she donned dark red cord jeans, a soft shirt in tiny red and cream checks and a sleeveless Fair Isle waistcoat. She brushed her hair until it shone and then pulled a beige wool bobble-hat over the unruly curls in the vain hope of keeping them under control in the fresh April breeze.

After a cursory breakfast—she was far too het up to eat—she grabbed her bag and red waterproof jacket and set off purposefully in the direction of her car. Simon's rangy figure lounged in the doorway of the caravan, sending a final encouraging wave as she drove off. His expression was its usual laconic self, but there was a clear gleam in his eyes as he wished her luck.

Her spirits soared as she drove through green sweeps of awakening countryside. April showers had brought grass and trees to verdant luxury. Daffodils bloomed on manicured village lawns; dandelions and daisies decorated lush fields; dripping cherry and hawthorn blossom painted hedgerows pink and white; thickening verges sported a froth of cow-parsley and clumps of golden primroses. It was too soon for the cows to be out, but plenty of sheep and lambs dotted the hillsides.

Josie warmed to this part of the country as it sparkled through a filter of early sunshine. Yes, she could belong here. She was doing the right thing, accepting this job—whatever else was going to happen. And today she would make sure she knew more about that, one way or another. Today was the beginning of the rest of her life!

This morning she was propelled by instinct, perhaps even impulse. The new Josie was learning how to follow her heart rather than her head. It was a strange, untried experience, bound to feel frightening—but exhilarating, exciting ... real: and she knew for sure it was leading her in the right direction at this moment.

As she hit the suburbs of the ancient city of Bath, she opened a street map out on the passenger seat. It was going to be quite tricky, negotiating those convoluted one-way systems, and she did not not know her way round the place well.

She knew from her map that Alex's firm had its offices down by the River Avon where it winds round the back of the old city. What she did not realise until she got there was that it occupied part of a disused warehouse. The rambling, dignified building had been converted into three units, each housing a separate business enterprise. She parked the 2CV in a cobbled yard which sloped down to the river, and consulted the sign at the main door which informed her that Grant Randle Holt's premises were at the top.

The lift was one of the old-fashioned kind with heavy iron gates you had to pull back—but smooth and streamlined, its old wood beautifully polished, its metal gleaming. In two minutes it was depositing her at the third floor, and she stepped out—pulse racing, heart pounding but outwardly cool.

There was no door or corridor. She stood at the edge of a huge open-plan studio which must have covered the whole area of the building. Vast expanses of plate glass took up most of the walls and some of the roof as well, bringing in wide vistas of the city and its surrounding hills, flooding the room with clear, sharp light. Up here there was nothing old-fashioned about the furniture or fittings, which represented the best in modern simplicity. Josie was no expert, but she recognised a carefully balanced blend of comfort and taste. It was a peaceful, airy place—a place where you could relax and work at the same time.

Several people were busy now doing just that, each perched on a high stool at an individual wooden desk, deep in concentration. Josie's glance flickered over them seeking out the one face and form which would stand out from the rest. But he was not there. She could tell that anyway from the atmosphere, as soon as she arrived—it had his stamp on it, a sense of him about it, but Alex was not there.

Vicky Randle was, though; she spotted Josie and jumped down from her stool, homing in on her as she hovered uncertainly at the sidelines. Vicky was her working self today, smartly attractive in a navy pinafore dress over a pale blue rollneck jumper, her short fair hair neat, her face half hidden behind large round spectacles.

'Josie!' She positively beamed a welcome that had to be sincere. 'What a nice surprise! What brings you among us? Were we expecting you?'

'Well, no,' Josie admitted. 'I was passing this way,' she lied, 'and I thought I'd just look in and see if . . .'

'I'm afraid Alex is out.' Vicky was so natural, you would have thought it was the most routine thing in the world for Josie to call in. 'He's tramping about some massive plot—a sports complex or recreation club, I think it's going to be—we haven't had the tender accepted yet. He should be back around lunchtime. Can you come back then, or would you like to wait? You're very welcome,' she urged.

'Well, I . . .' Foolishly, Josie felt caught out. She stupidly hadn't planned on this: why shouldn't Alex be out of the office, after all? She should have phoned first but somehow she had not been able to bring herself to do it, Disembodied voices were so difficult. This was something she knew she would have to sort out face to face. 'I'm not in a hurry,' she told Vicky now.

Vicky had been summing her up: the keyed-up

expression, the air of nervous hesitation; and immediately took charge. 'I'll tell you what. I'm not too busy this morning. Stay and have a cup of coffee and a chat—see round a bit—peep at the Summerford plans. I'm afraid,' she added wickedly, 'there isn't a model of the site.'

Josie had the grace to blush at this gently wry dig; but she nodded gratefully and smiled in reply to Vicky's invitation. 'Thank you,' she said. 'I'd like that very much. I'd like to see those plans, and anything else you're doing, if you can really spare the time.' She gazed about the studio in genuine fascination, her feline eyes luminous in the bright light.

'I can always spare time from hard graft,' Vicky said. 'Any excuse to malinger. Lazy is my middle name,' Josie laughed, disbelieving every word of it; but Vicky went on: 'Not like Alex—he's the glutton for work.'

'Yes,' Josie said. 'You told me.'

'So I did.' Vicky turned and began to lead her through the room towards a far corner, where a small group of low armchairs clustered invitingly round a glass-topped coffee table. 'I was forgetting. Mind you,' she added, over her shoulder, 'he has seemed a bit—abstracted lately. We're hoping he isn't sickening for something.'

Josie chose not to comment on this. Something in Vicky's tone led her to hope, just a little; but she was not jumping to conclusions—not any more—not until she had the chance to confront him, face to face.

Heads popped up as they passed the desks—friendly, interested eyes candidly scrutinising this stranger in their midst. Vicky paused to introduce Josie to each person separately. 'Josie, this is Sue Clements, our interior designer. What she doesn't know about fabrics, paints and wallpapers has yet to be invented. And this is Ruth Short, our assistant—destined for great things, whether with us or not.' The two young women greeted Josie warmly before getting on with their drawings and colour schemes.

Vicky stopped at another desk: 'And this is Julian Holt, our Junior Partner and resident whizz-kid. The up-and-coming generation. Jule, this is Josie.' She peered over his shoulder. 'What's that you're working on?'

Julian treated Josie to a dazzling beam, crammed with teeth. He was very young—probably, she thought, younger than herself; compactly built and extremely goodlooking in a slick kind of way. Everything about him, from shoes to clothes to bristling hairstyle—including the one gold earring—was meticulously geared to the latest trends. But he had an open, honest expression and sharp grey eyes—which were busy, at this moment, on her face.

'Ideas for the Hammond factory,' he told Vicky, without looking at her. 'Hi, Josie,' he went on. 'Where did you spring from? I haven't seen you before, have I?'

'No,' Josie agreed, returning his direct inspection.

'I thought not, I'd be sure to remember if I had.' He turned to Vicky. 'Friend of yours?' he demanded. 'If so, why haven't you produced her before? It's hardly fair to us predatory males,' he complained, 'if you hide the best ones away.' He transferred his attention back to Josie. 'Is it, darling?' he grinned.

Josie stifled an answering grin at this piece of outrageously sexist flirtation. Before she could find a suitable retort, Vicky was wading in on her behalf. 'Don't you start on all that smooth talk, young Jule. Josie's a high-powered professional person, not some fluffy chick for you to practise your lines of chat on.'

He was totally unabashed. 'Brainy as well as beautiful, no less? So, who's complaining? What's your line, doll? Let me guess . . .' putting his head on one side, he studied her cheekily. 'Hmmm—I can see you as a doctor, stunning in the white; or perhaps a bewigged lawyer, taking the courtroom by storm. No . . . no, I've got it—you're a teacher! That's it—a professor in the making—holding a class enthralled in the palm of your hand . . .'

'No.' Josie refused to enlighten him. She was rather enjoying his little games; they made a change, after life's recent solemnities.

'She's an archaeologist, Jule.' Vicky wagged a finger at him, like a starchy schoolmistress herself. 'Summerford?' she prompted, expecting him to take the point.

'Ah—*that* Josie.' His inspection intensified. 'Your name has been much on the lips of our lord and master of late,' he told her. 'Now that I see you,' he added cryptically, 'I can understand why.'

Josie could have wished he had phrased his remarks slightly differently. As it was, they caused a distinct shiver to run up her spine.

Sensing her reaction, Vicky took her gently by the elbow. 'Come on, Josie. We must let little Jule get on with his drawing, otherwise the creative process will dry up.'

'And we wouldn't want that, now would we?' Julian shrugged and grinned; then he turned back to his desk. 'See you around, Josie. Don't make your first visit here your last. Always good to see a bit of fresh talent about the old place.'

'Incorrigible!' muttered Vicky as they walked away; but she was smiling. 'Quick mind—clever designer,' she murmured in Josie's ear as they made their way to the end of the studio. 'He's got a shining future—Alex was right to give him the break and make him a partner, though I had my doubts. It's really brought him on— hardened his attitude. He's an asset to the firm already. Just needs to grow up a bit, that's all!'

'We all have to do that in our own time,' Josie found herself observing wisely. Apart from a brief, sharp glance, Vicky made no comment.

In the corner, well away from the rest, a pretty dark girl sat behind a wide office desk, surrounded by the usual clutter of files and documents, typewriter and telephone. 'This,' Vicky said, 'is our super-secretary, Linda. This whole outfit would fall apart completely without her. Linda, this is Josie Barnes.'

Linda smiled over her stack of paperwork. 'Did you say Barnes?'

'That's right,' Josie confirmed, half-expecting what was coming next.

Linda frowned, fixing hazel eyes on Josie. 'Now where have I heard that name?'

'Summerford Project?' Vicky suggested.

'I'm the archaeologist there,' Josie explained politely—wondering whether there was anyone there who had missed out on the unfolding saga.

'Ah, yes.' Linda nodded sagely. 'The one that's been causing all the uproar in the last few days—something about Wallace Holdings? I'm not well up on the details, but I know I've had to put through a lot of urgent phone calls, and send off express-delivery packages, and make endless cups of black coffee for Mr Grant, and generally try to calm him down while he sorted some knotty problem out.' She eyed Josie with friendly curiosity. 'Must have been pretty important, to get Mr Grant as worked up as that. He doesn't usually . . .'

'It was important,' confirmed Josie, feeling her cheeks heat up as she heard the extent of Alex's involvement. Just how wrong about him had she been? Just how much humble pie was she going to have to eat?

'Talking of coffee,' Vicky interrupted briskly—perhaps protecting Josie from further uncomfortable revelations, 'could you rustle up an extra cup for Josie, please love? I'm going to show her some plans; and we've got a few things to talk over—haven't we, Josie?'

'Yes,' Josie agreed. 'I rather think we have.'

Ten minutes later the two of them were ensconced in plush armchairs, sipping coffee from chunky earthenware mugs. Their low tones were muffled in that well-upholstered corner, but a certain amount of movement and chatter from behind them indicated that everyone else was also taking a coffee-break.

'So,' Vicky eyed Josie over the rim of her cup; 'you must be delighted with the latest bit of news?'

Josie braced herself to meet this subject head-on at last. 'Yes, of course I am. I haven't heard it officially yet, actually. Someone from the Commission phoned me yesterday about something else, and . . .'

Vicky's eyebrows lifted. 'You mean Wallace Holdings haven't even *told* you yet? I'd have thought they'd put you out of your misery before anyone else.'

'Would you?' Josie muttered cynically. 'I should think they'd be only too glad to let me stew as long as possible.' Taking a fortifying swig of coffee, she leaned towards Vicky, her expression suddenly intense. 'Vicky, how did he—how did you do it? I don't understand. It must have been something to do with you . . .'

'It was Alex, of course.' Vicky stared thoughtfully down into her coffee mug. 'In a way, it's a good thing you didn't catch him here this morning. Gives me a chance to put you in the picture. I think I'd do it more—comprehensively than he would. He's not the man to blow his own trumpet, even when it's deserved.'

Josie nodded, her eyes expectantly bright. 'I knew it was him. I mean . . .' she blushed slightly, 'I know now.'

'Yes, well,' Vicky said, a wry edge to her voice, 'I'd better start at the beginning. If I repeat things Alex has already told you—well,' she pointed out, 'then you'll know he was telling you the truth.'

And this time, Josie's mind twisted the knife in the wound, *you might even believe it*.

Vicky leaned back in her chair, her blue eyes on Josie's face; 'When we first heard the plan about building time being brought forward, we weren't too upset or surprised, because we'd actually made that recommendation ourselves—as Alex said at the meeting. We'd been given to understand, Josie, that your Project was nearly finished anyway, and that nothing would be badly disrupted if it was cut short. And that,' she emphasised, 'is the truth.'

Of course it was the truth. Wallace Holdings would say anything to get things going their way; Josie should have guessed that.

'We gave the okay,' Vicky went on, 'because the sooner our plans are implemented the closer we can all keep to our estimates—and the sooner we get paid. After the decision was made, Alex said he'd better go and take another look round the site, in case we needed to make any alterations to our original plans. After all, it had been a year since we'd seen it. He chose a Sunday morning, when he knew plenty of other people were usually around—members of the public he could merge with, wander among . . . he was quite chary of meeting you, thinking you'd have had the news and you wouldn't like it. Anyway, he arrived a bit early—and there you were, all alone . . .'

'There I was,' echoed Josie, who recalled that moment all too vividly.

'And there was all your hard work, and your keen helpers, and your achievements—and you made it quite plain to Alex that you needed, and still expected, every day of that year you were still supposed to have.'

'If only he'd told me the reason he was there, straight away,' murmured Josie.

'He just couldn't believe the company hadn't told you yet. He decided to talk it over with me before saying anything. He came rushing over in a state of high indignation on your behalf, raving about the dig, slanging the company . . . and, well,' she smiled, 'the rest is history.'

'You descended on me with your fine brood,' Josie remembered, returning the smile, 'and I thought you were . . .' her face went pink. Now she had started all this blushing and crying again, it seemed she was doomed to do it rather a lot of the time.

Vicky chuckled. 'Quite understandably, you thought

we belonged to Alex. He was in such a tizz, he never thought to explain all that first: to you or me. Anyway, we saw round and I felt just as he did. As soon as we got to work on the Monday we were on to Wallace Holdings, telling them to hold everything while we revised our plans—we didn't say why, just that we wanted another few days before the proposal was finally implemented. We also ascertained that they hadn't actually told you yet.' She pursed up her lips. 'They weren't best pleased with us—said it was unprofessional behaviour, and why hadn't we considered this before. Alex didn't like that one bit. He takes a lot of pride in his work, and he came in for all the stick, being the big boss.'

Josie winced: on top of that, he had taken more stick from her. 'Go on,' she implored, grimly determined to hear the full facts from this involved observer.

'Well, let me see . . . by the Tuesday we hadn't come up with a satisfactory solution, so we agreed we owed it to you to tell you the truth, since Wallace Holdings didn't seem to be going to yet. Alex couldn't bear to think of you there, working so hard and not knowing the facts . . . so he went over there, didn't he, and paid you a visit?'

'We went out to supper. It was a—a very nice evening. But he didn't tell me.'

'No. He did intend to—he did try. But when he heard about your latest news—those graves, wasn't it?—he determined all over again to get something sorted out—some kind of compromise—before you had to know what was going on. Alex isn't one to give in easily; and it was so obvious you needed all those months to complete this recent discovery . . . so he didn't tell you, after all. He came back to me, and we started all over again, juggling with the plans, discussing the possibilities.'

'Meanwhile, I heard the news the next day,' Josie remembered painfully, 'and I immediately assumed he was—you were—all part of the plot . . . all in it together . . .'

'So I gathered.' Vicky sighed. 'I could hardly blame you. It must have been an incredible blow. Well, we knew you'd had the letter—a secretary at W. H. told us it had been sent off. So Alex went round to see you again, hoping to tell you that at least we were trying to find a way round it—that you shouldn't despair. We still didn't know how, but we had to find a way which wouldn't ruin our professional pride.'

'And I didn't even hear him out!' Josie's voice was very low. 'So—after that?'

'Well,' Vicky considered. 'On the Friday morning, before the meeting, he came up with an idea—and we went straight over to the contractors with it.'

'But what was it?' Josie found herself fascinated—quite apart from the vital bearing it had on her own project's future.

'The best way I can answer that is by showing you the plans. To put it simply, he realised it should be possible—with a bit of manipulation—to start work on the main foundations and footings for the actual houses without tampering with more than one outer strip of your field. You see,' she explained, 'it just happens that some of your site is destined to be grounds and gardens—children's play area, pool and all that. My beautiful landscaping.' She grinned.

Josie began to understand. 'But—what did the contractors say?'

A shadow of irritation crossed Vicky's brow as she recalled what had obviously been a tricky session. 'They were intransigent. Insisted there was no way they could leave out one bit of preparation work till later. If their machines were moving in, they were moving in to the whole thing. They wouldn't budge an inch.'

'Poor you. So that's why you arrived so late at the meeting . . .'

'And why we were a bit—fraught, yes,' Vicky endorsed. 'It was a heavy day.'

It had certainly been that, for all concerned. No wonder Alex had reacted as he had to her, afterwards, when she had once again refused to listen to him. 'But they changed their minds later—why?'

Vicky relaxed, coming to a more pleasant part of her tale. 'Alex and I discussed the whole thing far into that night. When he finally got back, he came round to our house for supper and we were still scratching our heads over it at midnight. John went to bed and left us to it.'

'Oh dear!' Josie was forcing herself to remember how Alex had said, that afternoon, he had to get back to Bath to talk to Vicky. God, what an idiot she had been altogether! She could hardly bear it—but she had come here to learn the full facts, and she was not running away from them now. Any of them—personal or otherwise.

Vicky was thinking of her husband, an affectionate smile playing on her face. 'Oh—don't worry about John. He's used to it, and sometimes I don't see him half the night, anyway, when he's writing.'

'But you came up with a better solution in the end?' Josie prompted eagerly.

'Alex did. He worked at it right through the weekend with hardly a break. You wouldn't credit how much hard graft it takes to alter even a small thing on a plan—especially where actual houses are involved. Fortunately, there were only about two—and he's shifted those up so that only the very edge of your field is actually built on. Most of it will now be just environmental landscaping, and there's no real need to prepare the ground for that till the buildings are up. It was a marathon operation, Josie, believe me.'

She believed it well enough—now. And when Alex had visited her on Saturday, he had been in the middle of all that—but he hadn't even mentioned the plans.

He'd had other matters on his mind just then. 'I can imagine,' she muttered, colouring.

Vicky smiled. 'We bore the new plans in triumph to the contractors first thing Monday. This time, by great good luck, we got hold of a different director—much more sympathetic. He looked at them carefully and said he didn't see why the rest shouldn't go ahead, leaving your little section till the very last—bound to be nine months from when they start, at least. Actually, he became quite interested and upset about your Project, when we explained. If we'd got him on our side in the first place . . .' she sighed. 'But I think he was away on holiday or something.'

Josie pictured their moment of success. 'You must have been over the moon!' They had worked so hard to earn it—and all on account of her.

'You could say so. Tired—but thrilled.' Her blue eyes were kind as she smiled at Josie. 'Alex is normally the most peaceable, even-tempered soul. But just occasionally he gets really worked up over something, and then he's like a tornado.' She was watching Josie closely. 'I wouldn't like to cross him at a time like that.' No, Josie thought; you would not! 'But no one I know could make a better ally, Josie. And the fact that he inadvertently helped to get you into the mess in the first place only made him all the more determined to get you out of it. Once he'd seen the Project in action . . . and met you . . .' she paused, her head on one side. 'I don't quite know what got into him, to be honest. I've never seen him so desperate to achieve anything. And I've known him a good few years, up against some tough challenges.'

'Yes. Well.' Once again, Josie had to clear her throat, which appeared to have been taken over by a frog. 'So—Wallace Holdings had to agree in the end?'

'If that was what their contractors said. Anyway it's no skin off their nose. The scheme still goes ahead in three months' time—only your bit of it doesn't have to be touched then. So it works out okay for everyone. I mean, there'll be bulldozers sullying your nearer horizon for a while—you'll even be able to see the houses taking shape—but I don't think it should bother you at all.'

'Might be quite interesting,' Josie said warmly. 'Vicky, I—I don't know how to thank you.'

'Not me, love. I just got carried along in the great man's wake; thank him.' She leaned forward, adopting a conspiratorial air. 'He'll be glad you came. He was very upset when you wouldn't believe in his good intentions. Alex comes from one of those braw Scots tribes where they all speak their minds and tell it like it is. They're also the warmest, most supportive and sincere people I've ever met. He might have lived down here in the sophisticated south for many years, but he's still a vibrant, hot-blooded Celt at heart. And his heart still rules, Josie—despite that original mind and hard head.' She was silent for a few moments, gazing up through a skylight at the blue dome that might have been only just on the outside of it. 'How he's avoided giving it away to some lucky lady all these years, I can't imagine. He always says he's never met one that would have him. But plenty have tried—I suspect he's never met one who was good enough for him.'

The message could hardly have been clearer if she had shouted it from the rafters. *Hang on to him, girl,* Vicky was telling her, loudly. *You're the lucky one.*

Don't worry, Josie thought, as a rush of pure emotion threatened to engulf her. I get the message. 'Perhaps,' she said quietly, 'such a paragon doesn't exist.'

Vicky grinned directly at her. 'Oh yes she does. And when Alex is ready, he'll find her. Now,' she became brisk. 'How about a look at these plans?'

'Yes, please.' Josie stood up. Her legs wobbled a bit, her knees felt weak, as if she had received a shock. Well, in a way she had—and it was not over yet: she still had to face the man himself.

She did not have to wait long. As they stood in front of the huge notice board which covered the whole of one inner wall, poring over the revised plan for the Summerford development, a firm tread came up behind them, a familiar deep voice cut through their concentration.

'Two of my favourite ladies!' Alex pushed between them so that he could put an arm round each waist. 'Good to see you, Josie. Admiring my handiwork?'

From his attitude, you would think she dropped in here every day! It was as if the scenes in the caravan had never taken place. But not for Josie: she froze under his touch, her heart hammering in her throat, her voice deserting her altogether. She stared straight ahead, unable even to look at him.

Vicky came to her rescue. 'Alex! You're back earlier than I expected. Josie came by hoping to see you. I've just been telling her all about how we beat the system and got her off the hook. Now I'm showing her how we—how *you*—did it.'

His arm was tightening on her body, pulling her hard against his own firm contours. Still she kept her eyes fixed on the plans, away from him. Words seemed to be expected of her, and she found them somehow. 'They—the Commission only phoned me yesterday. I—I had no idea till then.' With a supreme effort she forced her head round and up, at last looking into the dark eyes—which looked inscrutably back. 'Thank you, Alex,' she breathed. There, it was said. At least it was a start.

He nodded, his expression softening—telling her he knew she was acknowledging more, much more, than that. The lines of his face were warm as he smiled down at her. She responded to the smile from parts of her which had never, till that second, been alive. 'No, Josie. It was the least I could do, after my part in the original decision. I felt I owed it to you,' he paused, 'compromise—remember?'

'Well,' she all but whispered, 'I'm grateful—whatever the reason.'

Their gazes seemed rivetted together. Vicky broke the tight thread of tension, pointing to a separate sheet depicting the interior layouts of the new homes. 'What do you think of these, then, Josie? I have to hand it to you, Alex—I wouldn't say no to one of these myself, and I've always preferred older houses.' Proudly she took Josie on a guided tour of the diagrams, like an enthusiastic estate agent. 'See, they've all got these fantastic heating and insulation devices; integrated decor to your choice, two to five bedrooms, sunken baths, split-level living rooms. The lot! And it's not like most estates, either,' she went on eagerly. 'They're all separate and different from each other. Not forgetting,' she concluded triumphantly, 'my superbly landscaped grounds.'

'Spare your own blushes, at least, Mrs Randle,' Alex observed with a grin.

'Why should I?' Vicky retorted. 'False modesty's a waste of time. It's one of our best, and you know it. Come on Josie—you'd like to see the pictures of my gorgeous gardens, wouldn't you?'

Josie was in the grip of a strange kind of elated relief, laughing at them both. 'Of course. I'm sure they're lovely.'

'There you are!' Vicky extricated herself from Alex's arm and moved along until she stood opposite some exterior plans. Alex followed, drawing Josie gently after him.

'They're very fine, Vicky. The whole thing's—well, it's wonderful.' It was positively mouth-watering, in Josie's humble opinion. She supposed you would have to be very rich indeed, even to contemplate living in such an up-market development.

Perhaps Alex had been reading her mind. 'As a matter of fact,' he proclaimed coolly, 'I'm thinking of putting in for one of them myself.'

Both women turned on him at this pronouncement. 'Alex—you're not serious!' Vicky was openly torn between horrified disbelief and incipient envy. 'They'll cost . . .!'

'No more than I can afford,' he countered. 'I'm fed up with my tatty little flat—and it's hardly much of an advert for my trade. I'm too busy with other people's homes to bother about my own, and I think it's time I did something about that. Also I feel a need for wide open spaces around me—inside and out,' he confided. 'And a bit of creature comfort never did a man any harm. I reckon I deserve a more salubrious pad, in my mature years.'

Vicky snorted. 'We've both got a long way to go before middle-age sets in. But Alex,' she pressed, '*are* you serious? I mean—do you really think it'd suit you?'

'Never more so. Good lord,' he pointed out, 'I designed the damn things! If I can't live in one of them, who can? It's high time I took on a few responsibilities,' he went on vaguely. 'Mortgages, for instance. Anyway,' he grinned mischievously, 'I've become sort of attached to that spot. What do *you* think, Josie?' he challenged. 'Do you disapprove too? do you think I've gone clean off my chump—as my respected partner here so obviously does?'

Josie who had been absorbing all this with a crazy jangle of mixed feelings, swallowed hard. 'I think . . . I think you're very lucky, and very clever,' she said slowly. 'I'd do the same myself, if I could afford it.'

'And if you were staying around this neck of the woods.' Alex still had one arm round her, and she wondered if he had noticed her stiffening at these words. 'Well, I'm glad someone understands me, and doesn't think I'm selling out to the establishment. Or could it be,' he flashed a twinkling glance in Vicky's direction, 'that this esteemed partner of mine is just a wee mite jealous?'

Vicky laughed. 'Maybe I am, at that.'

'Now, ladies.' Alex took a step back, swinging them both round to face him. 'I don't know about you, but I'm in need of some sustenance. Josie,' he declared, 'I'm taking you out. We've got several matters to talk over, haven't we?' His tone was light, but his eyes were intent, piercing, on hers.

'Yes, Alex,' she acknowledged meekly. It had to come, she knew that.

He turned to Vicky. 'Mrs Randle?'

'Mr Grant?'

'Will you hold the fort while I play hookey for part of this afternoon? I feel an extended lunch-hour coming over me.'

'Don't be a fool—of course I will. Run along, my children, and enjoy yourselves.' Vicky laid a gentle hand on Josie's arm, smiling into the younger woman's shining green eyes. 'I'm sure I'll see you again very soon, Josie.'

'I hope so—and thanks for . . . for this morning, and everything,' Josie faltered.

'None needed,' Vicky transferred a prim glare on to Alex. 'As for you, partner—don't let me catch you on these premises again before tomorrow morning at the earliest. Understood?'

Alex schooled his lively features into earnest obedience. 'Yes, Ma'am,' he said.

CHAPTER TEN

THE spring morning had burgeoned into a golden day. As they strolled together, following the path of the river towards the heart of the city, Josie lifted her head and sniffed the air—as if to inhale the scent of promise it carried.

By common, wordless consent they stopped at a delicatessen to buy freshly-filled seedy rolls, succulent pastries, fruit, tomatoes. Then Alex led the way to a small green park, hidden away from the clamour of the streets; and they sat on a slatted wooden seat in a sunlit corner—secluded but not too far from where people and pigeons bustled about their daily business among bulbs and blossoms.

Their silence was easy, companionable, as if there were all the time in the world. Josie was aware of this sense of peace, and yet of reality, in his company. But there was still a major challenge to be faced, and very soon. She must not let herself give in to that heady sensation of happiness and security—not yet. She must keep it at bay until she was as sure of him as she was of herself.

When they had eaten the last juicy orange, licked their sticky fingers and wiped them on Alex's clean handkerchief, he leaned back, sighed and closed his eyes, turning his face up to greet the sun. At the same time he reached an arm around her, pulling her head against his shoulder, nuzzling the top of her glossy hair with his bearded chin. She could feel his breath stirring in her auburn curls; her cheek felt soft against the coarse weave of his jacket. Her heart was full to bursting; her body tingled with unspoken messages.

But they could not remain unspoken any longer. 'Alex?' Her voice was cracked, husky.

'Josie?' Her own name rumbled through her, his very tone setting up its own intense vibrations.

'I just want to say, I—I'm sorry.'

'Ay.' The emotion of the moment searched out his Scottish roots. 'I know. I know, Josie; don't worry.'

He was trying to let her off lightly; but it would not do. 'No. Alex—I mean it. I . . . you were right; I've behaved like a silly schoolgirl. I've been behaving like one for years—ever since I was one, I suppose. I've never grown up, not properly. I thought I was so adult, so mature . . . but—I never really grew up.'

'Till now?' he suggested very softly, drawing her even closer.

'I—I've made a start,' she ventured, hesitantly.

'Oh, there's no doubt about that—you've made more than a start. You've made a breakthrough.' He sounded so sure; and yet so kind, so supportive, as if he knew how much it cost her to admit to these weaknesses. As if he knew, too, that a whole lot more had to come out yet.

Bravely, she persevered. 'All that crazy anger, Alex—it was never really directed at you. But you knew that, didn't you?'

'I hoped it wasn't,' Alex said simply.

'Vicky's been telling me exactly what really happened. Underneath I must have known it all the time, but it was as if . . . as if . . .'

'Yes?' he encouraged when she faltered.

'As if I desperately wanted to believe the worst. I didn't want to face up to what I owed you, or—or how I felt about you.' These last words came out almost on a whisper. Then she gathered strength and continued. 'I made myself think you were out to get what you could, walk all over me. I manufactured all that anger.'

He was silent for a full minute, his regular breathing calm against her. Then came the question she had expected and dreaded: quiet, unaggressive but right on target. 'Why, Josie?'

'Why?' Knowing full well what he meant, she played for time.

'*Why* all that empty rage? Why the warding-off of real feelings? Who is it you're really so furious with?' He paused, and when she made no reply, he added gently: 'What put it there—that grim streak across such a bright, passionate nature?'

There was no escape. She had to do it: wrench open a long-sealed door into a place where no one had ever even thought to glimpse, in all her adult life. 'I suppose—I thought I was over it, long ago; but I suppose it has to do with . . . my parents.'

Sensing her acute pain, he removed his arm from behind her back, laid his two hands on her shoulders and turned her—gently but firmly—to face him. Then he reached over and took one of her hands in both his, forcing the clenched fingers to uncurl from the tight knuckles they had made. Lifting the hand to his lips, he kissed the marks on the palm where her nails had dug into her skin.

'Go on.' His voice was very soft. She thought she had never seen any colour so warm, deep and dark as the rich brown of his eyes.

'My mother was a very—a very sweet person.' She flinched from the memory of that timid, withdrawn woman whom she had once cared so much about. 'She—we had some good times together. But she was always nervous, not very forceful, and my father . . .' Her eyelids dropped. This was going to be agonising, impossible.

But his finger was under her chin, raising her head to make her look at him. 'Your father?' He was still gentle—but demanding, even insistent.

She sucked in a harsh, rasping breath. 'He was a bully. Oh, not to me. He took precious little notice of me. It was her. He made her life a total misery.'

'How?' he pressed, when she threatened to dry up again.

'He went away for days at a time. He was a commercial traveller; I never even knew what in, I think it kept changing . . .' Now that she had started, the words came tumbling out in a jagged rush. 'And while he was away we were okay—we plodded on, nothing spectacular, but—you know . . .' she shrugged. 'Just life.'

'Then, when he came back?' He was relentless, it seemed, pushing her on.

'Every time he came back, it got worse. I was only little, and I escaped to my room, but I could hear them—my mother cried, sometimes all night; and he shouted, and he'd been drinking, I knew that by the smell and the way he . . . what he was like.'

Alex tried, with everything in him, to get at the truth. 'He beat her up? Used violence?'

'No—it wasn't physical—that was just it. He never risked anything that might make her run away and leave him. No, it was . . . mental cruelty. Emotional. A constant draining, nagging . . . haranguing her about everything she did, or tried to do. She was always wrong, everything about her was wrong. He kept on and on—making her feel smaller and more ineffectual than she already did.' Josie shivered, and Alex tightened his hold on her hand; but she was on her way now, gathering confidence. 'She seemed to shrivel into a tiny, wizened creature every time he was there. All I wanted to do was protect her from him, make him go away— but if I said anything he just shouted at me as well. I was so small . . .' She winced, once again that desperate little girl, overwhelmed with guilt and shame at her failure to help her beloved mother against this alien, raging male power.

'Poor little Josie.' Alex reacted—but carefully, his emotion controlled. 'And your poor, poor mother. And I dare say, if only one knew, your poor father as well,' he added unexpectedly.

Josie glanced up at him sharply. This was an angle

she had never considered. Perhaps even that unnatural monster of a man had had his problems, his griefs. Now that the whole ghastly snakepit was being forcibly revealed under its heavy stone, there was plenty to be faced . . . but not all at once; not yet.

As if tacitly understanding that, Alex said: 'What happened in the end?'

She gulped. The crunch was coming; it had to. 'When I was about fourteen, I suddenly realised why my mother put up with it; why she stayed around when all he did was make her life a hell on earth. I knew *I*'d have been off and away years ago,' she declared—green eyes blazing with recalled fury and defiance.

'And why was that?' he demanded quietly.

'She—she loved him.' Josie's fingers tried to tighten into fists again; but he prevented them, smoothing her sweating palms with his broad, dry thumbs. 'All through it—the torment, the degradation—she went on loving him. Sometimes, after they'd been at it for hours—him screaming, her sobbing—they'd disappear into their room and I . . . I knew what they were doing. Sometimes,' her voice dropped to a whisper, 'I heard that as well. I didn't know which was worse—the hate or the love. They seemed—the same thing, in the end.' She cleared her dry throat and raised her eyes to meet his again, with a new boldness. 'I decided, then and there, that if love did all that to you, it wasn't for me. Whatever else I might do with my life, I'd steer clear of that.'

'And who could blame you?' His voice was deliberately placid, but concern and sympathy were etched in every line of his handsome face. 'What became of them in the end, Josie? You told me your mother was dead. And your father?'

'In the end . . .' That was the hardest part of all, but she was not giving up now. 'When I was fifteen, and getting more involved with school and less with what went on at home—school was like a refuge, you see . . .'

He nodded. 'I began to notice that my mother was getting thinner and thinner—just sort of dwindling away in front of my eyes. She was still sweet and kind to me, but she seemed set apart—distant. When he came home and threw his weight about, she just sat there, staring at him, refusing to cry or—or react. That made him even worse, if anything.'

'Didn't anyone know what was going on?' Alex probed cautiously. 'Relatives—friends—neighbours?'

'We had no relatives within miles of London. My parents didn't go in for friends,' she recalled bitterly. 'If my mother got to know anyone, my father soon poured scorn—put a stop to it. As for neighbours, well, you know how it is in the great metropolis . . . everyone on top of each other, no one knowing or caring what goes on behind closed doors . . . and I was too proud to tell my friends or teachers.'

'Yes,' Alex observed, 'you would be.'

'Well, after that, when he saw he was—losing her, somehow, he started having other women, and telling her all the sordid details of these affairs . . .' She shuddered—her skin turning to gooseflesh even under the caress of the sun. 'It was horrible . . . horrible . . . I felt so angry, and sick, and frustrated. But what could I do? I hated him. I—I wished he'd drop dead.' There, the words were out; she had actually said it.

Alex was calmly taking in every phrase, every syllable, urging her on—knowing how vital it was to Josie to get it out of her system. 'But it wasn't him who did?' he prompted gently.

'Oh no.' She shook her head grimly. 'He just went on, and on. No; she was the one who died.' It was a bald statement—the plain, undecorated fact.

'How? When?' He was not letting her lose impetus now.

'She killed herself. One day, when I was away on a school trip—so that I wouldn't be upset, coming home and finding her.' Josie's laugh was hollow. 'She took an overdose of her sleeping pills and just slipped away. Or so they told me later. She suffered far less in death than she had in life, I've always tried to believe.'

'And your father? What happened to him?' Now that she had reached the crisis, Alex allowed himself to become pressing, almost urgent; but Josie felt oddly flat.

'I never saw him again. By the time I got home, he'd just—disappeared. No one ever found him. He never got in touch with me. For all I know, he may be dead as well. He never cared about me, anyway.' Her head lifted, jaw defiantly set.

Alex saw the whole situation, crystal clear. No wonder anger and rigid independence had become her only allies, her refuges in a bitter, hostile world—a world dominated, to her youthful eyes, by cruel, overbearing men. Who could blame her, in the end? His voice was low and restrained as he suggested: 'Perhaps he did love you both, in his way.'

She grunted expressively, casting her eyes down. 'You'd never have guessed it.'

He left it; there was plenty of time later to follow it up. 'What happened to you after—after that, Josie?' Get the story finished—for her sake, that was important.

'I'd lived inside a hard shell for years anyway; I just crawled even further in and closed up completely. No one could reach me; I had no intention of letting them.'

'Who tried?'

'Oh, various relations decided to appear on the scene, from hundreds of miles away—get me to go with them—but I wasn't having that. No way. I was staying on at school and taking my A-levels and going to college. I'd discovered the past—the reality of ancient history was so much better, and cleaner, and more . . . well, more *real* than the present. I knew that would have to be my life. And my school was very understanding.'

'But where did you live?'

'I was taken into care. They tried to make me go into a foster family, but I'd had enough of family life as I saw it; I refused to move. I stayed in the home for the next—oh, nearly three years. I don't remember much about it, really, I was so buried in my studies. Just continual noise; and kind, harassed people trying to do their best with difficult kids and scarce resources. I let it all wash over me till I got into Cambridge, and—well, I've stayed there ever since. For want of anywhere else to go, I suppose,' she concluded lamely.

'And the house? Your house? What happened to that?'

'The house?' She looked surprised. 'It wasn't ours; we rented it. My father left debts, not capital. I never had a penny of my own when it all . . . after it was all over.'

He was silent for several seconds, staring at her in compassionate comprehension. 'So,' he went on, his tone deliberately lighter, 'you took on the job of supervising the Summerford Project? Carried your shell over here with you?'

She smiled weakly. 'That's right. Little did I know, when I agreed to do the job, what it would mean to me in . . . other ways.'

'And little did I know,' he retorted, 'when I dropped by to inspect the site again, just what I'd be getting myself into.'

Now Josie was relaxing, at last. Leaning back, she closed her eyes, linking her hands behind her head as the sun's rays touched her pale skin. The poison was draining out, she could feel it. There was a cleansing—the unique relief of a lifetime's heavy burden shared and immediately halved.

Thank God she had met Alex. That he was—the person he was. Whatever happened after this, she would always have reason to be grateful to him for the last few days, and above all for this last hour.

He was close to her, speaking to her now—eager, intense. 'Josie, I know just how much it cost you to tell

me all that. It must have been an almighty struggle.
You've been incredibly brave—even braver than you
were all those years, fighting the world on your own.
Letting it out is the hardest bit.'

'I know.' She smiled. 'That's why I never did. I just—
fought them all off.'

'I expected a few nasties to crawl out of the
woodwork, once you got going, but I hadn't envisaged
anything quite as grim as this. You've had a rough
time, Josie—a lousy start. Makes me realise how lucky
I've been. It's only surprising you're as balanced and
beautiful as you are. But it's over now, and you'll find
you can face everything better—maybe even begin to
feel things again—now you've told me. Even if you feel
terrible now, you've done the right thing,' he assured
her earnestly.

'I don't feel terrible at all, Alex. I feel—released. I
know I've done the right thing.' Her voice was steady.
She opened her eyes and looked directly into his. 'I
know for sure.'

With one sensitive fingertip, he traced the line of her
profile, studying it. 'Now,' he said, 'it's my turn to
apologise.'

She frowned. 'What for? You've done nothing . . .'

'Saturday evening. My somewhat brutal methods of
breaking through those furious defences of yours. It
must have seemed barbaric to you—cruel,' his jaw
clenched, 'especially after what had happened three
nights earlier . . . But you'd better believe it was the
most painful, difficult thing I've ever set myself to do.'
His lips hardened to a tight line at the recollection.

She laid a light finger on them. 'No, Alex. It wasn't
cruel. It was kind, as only you know how to be. You
did it for my sake, I know that. If you hadn't chosen to
use those—shock tactics, I'd still be floundering in a sea
of bitterness and self-delusion. I hated you at the time,'
she confessed honestly. 'No man had ever treated me
like that before. But when I worked out why you'd

done it, I stopped hating you.' Her gaze intensified; green, iridescent on his face. 'I loved you for it. And I still do. And I always will,' she declared—defiantly, almost.

He took her finger from his lips and moved closer, catching both her hands in his. His voice had dropped to a low note—hoarse with stored passion. 'The next time,' he promised fervently, 'you won't get let off so lightly. Nothing—but nothing—is left in the world that can deter me from . . .'

'Bringing things to their natural conclusion?' she ventured, eyes gleaming.

'I would have put it more basically than that,' he admitted gruffly. 'But yes, you catch my drift. Next time—and it'll be soon—you won't know what's hit you.'

'Threat or promise?' she murmured dreamily—lashes lowering to veil the joy that lit her eyes.

'Whichever you like,' he countered, his hands tightening on hers.

'Next time,' she echoed, lifting her gaze once again to meet his.

'And all the other times,' he confirmed—vehement, confident, smiling down at her. Then he took her face between his hands and kissed her—sweetly, lingeringly. And despite the public setting, it was the most intensely intimate moment in Josie's life.

It was an afternoon of dappled sunshine, a haze of mutual happiness. Their joy was acute, illicit almost, so that surely it would sink with the sun, evaporate into a mirage. But it was real, it was solid—and it grew and deepened with each passing minute. Josie knew it; and in later years she was to look back on those magical hours as a tantalising foretaste of a whole new pattern of possibilities ahead, for them both.

They wandered about—mesmerised, like a pair of besotted tourists against the backdrop of that stately city, yet entirely wrapped up in one another so that its atmosphere invaded their sealed cocoon as if from far away. The elegant, curved Georgian terraces and crescents; the spacious neatness of squares and gardens; the mellow limestone façades, grey-gold in the spring sunlight—Josie had never really noticed it all before, but today they seemed stunningly fine: a natural landscape for the soaring new emotions that surged inside her.

She could feel at home here—she sensed that. Here was a place where she could put down roots. But then, Alex had lived here for years—and wherever he chose to be, she knew she would willingly follow. Seizing eagerly on the offer of a job in this area was just so much rationalisation. He was the reason she wanted to be here. What she felt for him transcended considerations of work, or location. Past, present and future— they had rolled themselves up into a single unit, for her; and he was at the heart of it. For her: but what about him? That was something she had yet to discover. That was an issue she must wait patiently to confront. When it was ready, it would be made clear.

Meanwhile Alex—lively, knowledgeable, alert even in his tender absorption—was busy supplying her with fascinating details about each set of buildings they passed. Eager to share with her his delight in his subject, his enthusiasm for his adopted territory, he pointed out architectural quirks and follies, recalled historical connections, recounted amusing anecdotes, described well-known literary figures. His central affection for humanity in general underlay everything he said; but it was tempered with that dry, understated humour which often reduced her to open, helpless laughter.

And Josie loved him all the more for it, reflecting privately that she could listen to those deep, soft tones all day—all her life—whatever they might be telling her.

They meandered along by the Roman Baths. 'Been to see them yet?' he enquired.

'No.' She felt slightly foolish. To have spent almost a year near the greatest natural hot springs in the country, and failed to visit them! 'I don't get much time off from the dig,' she explained defensively.

'You work too hard.' He squeezed her hand. 'You must close some weekends—take a break—I'll enjoy showing you round. You've got a lot to make up for, Miss Barnes, in more ways than one. And I'm the man to help you do it.'

She smiled up at him—hardly able to assimilate what was happening to her. 'Can you drink the water?' she asked—for something intelligent to say.

'Not any more; they declared it a health risk a few years back, after a child died from a virus thought to be picked up from it. You can't swim either. Shame, really: I always enjoyed imagining myself as a prosperous Roman in a toga, basking in all that comforting steam.'

'Attended by luscious slave girls?' she offered, entering into his mood at once.

'Luscious slaves of both sexes, I dare say,' he observed with a grin, 'knowing what the Romans got up to. You can still taste the water from another spring, though. They found one that wasn't contaminated. It's supposed to be full of health-giving properties. Cure things you never even knew you had.'

'I'd like to try that,' Josie mused. 'What's it like?'

'Like? Oh . . .' he was vague, offhand. 'Why don't we go and try some? I could do with a drink. You can get coffee as well.'

'I don't mind what we do,' Josie said happily. *As long as we do it together*, her heart took up the refrain—corny, but accurate.

'Come on then!' Swinging her hand, he led her a short distance further on to the Pump Room.

It was like walking into an earlier century—the seventeenth or eighteenth, Josie supposed, more recent history not being her strongest point, in here it was all cool dignified gentility. Even the presence of twentieth-century visitors could not undermine a strong impression that men and women in powdered wigs and painted faces, their clothes ornate and rustling, might appear at any moment—ready to exchange the latest gossip while they sipped the healthful minerals from the spa.

The atmosphere was heightened by trappings from the appropriate period: sedan chairs, chandeliers, discreet chamber-music in the background. Josie sat herself down on a Regency-style chair at a small table, glad to rest her legs, while Alex went to fetch tumblers of the specially bottled water.

Realising how thirsty she was, Josie took a generous swig from her glass. She did not notice that Alex had left his untouched on the table and was watching her with an expression of ironic amusement.

'*Ugh!*' She almost spat it out again, restraining herself just in time as the acrid, metallic taste hit her palate. 'Alex!' She slammed the glass down on the table top, wrinkling her nose in acute distaste. 'What *is* this stuff?'

'Best spring water, of course.' He was unruffled, regarding her solemnly.

'But it's revolting! More likely to kill than cure, judging by the taste.' She glared at him. 'You knew, didn't you? Look, you haven't even sipped yours! You—you monster—you might at least have warned me!' She lifted her glass and made as if to pour its contents right down his front, green eyes flashing sparks of mock rage.

He held up both hands in self-defence, grinning openly now. 'Okay! Okay! I submit, I confess, I led you on! I just had to see your face when you tried it. It was worth it, too, every second of it.' He chuckled, totally lacking in contrition. Then he seized the glass which hovered dangerously over his chest and forced her to set it down on the table, grabbing both her hands so that she could not renew the attack.

Josie was grinning too by this time. 'You're mean,' she accused gleefully. Then she softened graciously. 'I forgive you—thousands wouldn't.'

'I don't care about thousands, Josie.' Suddenly he was very serious. 'I only care about you. Do you really forgive me?' He hung his head.

'If you promise not to play fiendish tricks on me, ever again.' She hid her glowing eyes from him under lowered lashes.

'I promise.' He leaned over to kiss her softly on the eyes, the tip of the nose, the cheeks, the corner of the mouth—heedless of the company they were in. 'I'll always tell you the truth about everything. And I'll start here and now, with the most important truth of all. I love you, Josie. I've loved you since just about the first moment I laid eyes on you, across your field. I've loved you more with each new challenge you've thrown at me. I love everything I've learned about you.'

'Everything?' she breathed—her mind ranging painfully back over some of the more unfortunate displays of temperament she had subjected him to.

'Every single thing.' He smiled, reading her thoughts. 'So, from here on in, it can only get better . . . and I intend to learn a whole lot more about you yet.'

That was certainly one way of looking at it. If he could love her, having seen her in full strident action—warts and all—knowing every sordid fact there was to know about her life . . . She raised her eyes to meet his. 'Thank you, Alex.'

'Do stop thanking me, Josie. You've brought a new fire into my life, filled a gap. I can't lose you now. If there are speeches of thanks to be made, I've got just as much reason to make them. Let's take all that dull gratitude as read and concentrate on more . . . exciting channels of communication, eh?' His tone, low and suggestive, sent pulses throbbing through her body. Her hand, clasped in his, relayed tingling messages that were as new and yet as timeless as their love itself.

It was time to tell him that one last fact which she had been keeping back. How would he take it? In the present, she believed in his love: it was a shining, a tangible thing. But how did he see the future? She could not lose all that uncertainty, the product of years, in the space of a few hours.

'Alex,' she began, hesitantly.

'Not *more* secrets?' He bent to peer into her face. 'I know that tone. Come on, little lady—out with it—spill the beans.'

She told him, then. She told him about the Commission's offer, and her instant acceptance. She told him about her sense of belonging in this patch, even before the unforeseen turn of today's events. Then she sat, perfectly still and silent, waiting.

A succession of responses worked across his countenance as she spoke: incredulity, pleasure, admiration and—finally—delight. '*Josie!*' Several heads turned in their direction as the word burst out in a spontaneous flood of emotion. 'You're not just spirited and desirable—you're brilliant. You've just saved me the trouble of working out a devious scheme to woo you into staying around her after your year's up. I've been racking my brains to dream up some enticing professional niche for you—a bait, an offer you couldn't refuse, to pin you down—prevent you from going back to Cambridge.' She stared at him in amazement. Surely he must *know* she would have crossed the world for him? but then again, perhaps she had not made it very clear—up till now. 'I thought about wangling a job at Bath university for you . . . a specially set-up archaeological unit at Grant Randle Holt . . . bribing the local museums . . . but all I came up with was fixing you to my side with a ball and chain. And now . . . !'

'Now,' she assured him happily, 'I'm not going anywhere. I'm staying here.' His joy was so obviously genuine that it spilled over into her, and at last she believed in it—utterly certain of him; totally purged of all anxious secrets.

'With me?'

'As near as you'll let me be.' She was reticent, almost shy in her new-found honesty.

His smile spread ever further. 'If I had my way, you'd never be out of my sight. As a compromise,' he suggested, 'would you consider sharing that corner house I've marked out for myself on the Summerford site? I'd have rattled about in it, all on my own—but for Mr and Mrs Alexander Grant, it could be just ideal.'

At this unbelievable prospect, Josie dried up completely. She could only stare at him, eyes wide, lips slightly parted.

'Something wrong with my invitation? Am I pushing my luck—jumping the gun a bit?' He coughed and forced his expression into a satirical mask of formality. 'Miss Barnes, will you do me the inestimable honour of becoming my wife, sharing my humble abode?' he requested, in a style in keeping with their surroundings. 'Once it's been built, that is,' he added on a more pragmatic note.

She remained speechless. Thinking she still needed persuading, he increased the pressure. 'Just think of the suitability of the location,' he reminded her sardonically. 'I mean—where else would we live, you and I, but right there at the scene of our first private and public dramas? Among poignant memories and glorious countryside? And doesn't all that luxury—my award-winning design—tempt you, just a little?' he wheedled. 'Or did you intend to live in your caravan for ever?'

She found her voice at last; and it was clear, steady and tranquil. 'You know I'd live in a tent, if you were with me,' she told him truthfully. 'But yes, Alex—yes, please—I'll marry you, and live there with you. After the Project's over and the houses are built. Meanwhile . . .'

'Meanwhile,' he supplied, 'I'll play second fiddle to a whole load of bones, and bits of pottery, and devoted young thugs. Don't worry,' his grin was wry and affectionate, 'I know what I'm letting myself in for. I know my place.'

She returned the grin. 'That's not what I meant, and you know it, Alex. But I will have to stay on in the caravan till the dig's finished—most of the time. I'll get the more experienced members of my team to take over more often now—it's time they took a bit of responsibility—and I'll close up the site some weekends.' She coloured delicately. 'And you can come and stay there with me, as often as you like.'

'Try keeping me away.' Alex leaned across the table, seizing both her hands—at once intense again. She loved him for his energy, the wholeheartedness of his moods, his spark of enthusiasm behind the gentle irony. 'Josie, that development is my best piece of work to date. Some extra inspiration seemed to guide me as I was doing it. When I heard that an ancient settlement had been found there, I thought perhaps that was what made the place special. Now I know what it was.'

Josie gazed at him, enquiring. 'Tell me.'

'It's quite simple. I hadn't met you yet, but some part of me knew you were coming. I designed those houses for you. And one day,' he promised ardently, 'I shall build you a home which really is something else. Something out of this world. Somewhere we can live for the rest of our lives; where no family could help but be happy.'

She smiled, from the depth of her love for him. 'Thank you, Alex.'

He groaned, releasing one hand to clutch his head. 'How do I get this woman to give over thanking me?' Then he kissed her again—deeply and thoroughly this time. When he had finished, he sat back and surveyed her through dark eyes whose profound warmth she seemed to have known all her life.

Then he was on his feet, picking up the two rejected tumblers of spa water and raising one of them in a cheerful salute. 'Time to throw all that old bitterness down the drain, I think,' he declared, 'and replace it with something sweet and tasty and infinitely more palatable.'

'A cup of coffee and a piece of cake?' she suggested hopefully.

'Exactly,' he said.

ROMANCE

Next month's romances from Mills & Boon

Each month, you can choose from a world of variety in romance with Mills & Boon. These are the new titles to look out for next month.

BOND OF VENGEANCE Jessica Steele
CALIFORNIA DREAMING Sara Francis
SWEET TEMPEST Helen Bianchin
LEGALLY BOUND Kerry Allyne
THE PASSIONATE ESCAPE Mary Lyons
A NAKED FLAME Charlotte Lamb
TOO FAR, TOO FAST Elizabeth Oldfield
YEAR'S HAPPY ENDING Betty Neels
VIKING INVADER Sally Wentworth
WANTING Penny Jordan
ONCE A LOVER Claire Harrison
RUN SO FAR Peggy Nicholson

Buy them from your usual paperback stockist, or write to: Mills & Boon Reader Service, P.O. Box 236, Thornton Rd, Croydon, Surrey CR9 3RU, England. Readers in South Africa-write to: Mills & Boon Reader Service of Southern Africa, Private Bag X3010, Randburg, 2125.

Mills & Boon
the rose of romance

Mills Boon

Take 4
Exciting Books
Absolutely
FREE

Love, romance, intrigue... all are captured for you by Mills & Boon's top-selling authors. By becoming a regular reader of Mills & Boon's Romances you can enjoy 6 superb new titles every month plus a whole range of special benefits: your very own personal membership card, a free monthly newsletter packed with recipes, competitions, exclusive book offers and a monthly guide to the stars, plus extra bargain offers and big cash savings.

**AND an Introductory FREE GIFT for YOU.
Turn over the page for details.**

As a special introduction we will send you four exciting Mills & Boon Romances Free and without obligation when you complete and return this coupon.

At the same time we will reserve a subscription to Mills & Boon Reader Service for you. Every month, you will receive 6 of the very latest novels by leading Romantic Fiction authors, delivered direct to your door. You don't pay extra for delivery — postage and packing is always completely Free. There is no obligation or commitment — you can cancel your subscription at any time.

You have nothing to lose and a whole world of romance to gain.

Just fill in and post the coupon today to **MILLS & BOON READER SERVICE, FREEPOST, P.O. BOX 236, CROYDON, SURREY CR9 9EL.**

Please Note:- **READERS IN SOUTH AFRICA** write to **Mills & Boon, Postbag X3010, Randburg 2125, S. Africa.**

FREE BOOKS CERTIFICATE

To: Mills & Boon Reader Service, FREEPOST, P.O. Box 236, Croydon, Surrey CR9 9EL.

Please send me, free and without obligation, four Mills & Boon Romances, and reserve a Reader Service Subscription for me. If I decide to subscribe I shall, from the beginning of the month following my free parcel of books, receive six new books each month for £6.60, post and packing free. If I decide not to subscribe, I shall write to you within 10 days. The free books are mine to keep in any case. I understand that I may cancel my subscription at any time simply by writing to you. I am over 18 years of age.

Please write in BLOCK CAPITALS.

Signature _____

Name _____

Address _____

_____ Post code _____

SEND NO MONEY — TAKE NO RISKS.

Please don't forget to include your Postcode.

Remember, postcodes speed delivery. Offer applies in UK only and is not valid to present subscribers. Mills & Boon reserve the right to exercise discretion in granting membership. If price changes are necessary you will be notified.

6R   *Offer expires December 31st 1984*

EP8